Automatic Flight Control

E. H. J. Pallett, T.Eng. (CEI), A.M.R.Ae.S., F.S.L.A.E.T.

GRANADA
London Toronto Sydney New York

Granada Publishing Limited–Technical Books Division
Frogmore, St Albans, Herts AL2 2NF
and
3 Upper James Street, London, W1R 4BP
866 United Nations Plaza, New York, NY 10017, USA
117 York Street, Sydney, NSW 2000, Australia
100 Skyway Avenue, Rexdale, Ontario, M9W 3A6, Canada
PO Box 84165, Greenside, 2034 Johannesburg, South Africa
CML Centre, Queen & Wyndham, Auckland 1, New Zealand

Copyright © E. H. J. Pallett, 1979

ISBN 0 246 11167 4

First published by Granada Publishing Limited 1979

Printed in Great Britain by William Clowes & Sons Limited,
Beccles and London

Granada ®
Granada Publishing ®

Contents

Preface

At the present time there is hardly an aircraft in either civil or military operation without some form of automatic flight control system comprising part of its standard operational equipment. The systems available are as diverse as the aircraft themselves, varying from a simple roll stabiliser or 'wing-leveller' in a single-engined private aircraft, to the sophisticated flight-guidance systems capable of automatically controlling the flight paths of large transport aircraft from take-off to touchdown and roll-out. It is then a little difficult perhaps to realise that the development of such systems has arisen from foundations laid years before man himself took to the air to become the controller of his own 'flight path destiny'.

The early inventors of 'heavier-than-air flyling machines' were, of course, faced with many problems, the most prominant of which was the one associated with the attainment of stabilised flight. Although there was an awareness that stability should be inherent in the basic design of a machine, little was known of the separation of stability into dynamic and static elements in relation to the various degrees of freedom possessed by a machine. As a result, and as recorded history indicates, efforts were directed more towards keeping a machine straight and level and free from the effects of external disturbances, and to derive the requisite stability by applying some form of artificial stabilising device.

It is of interest to note that possibly the first machine to use such a device was an unmanned glider designed by the Frenchman Charles Renard in 1873. The device consisted of a transverse pendulum coupled to two 'steering wings', the idea being that if the machine turned from its intended flight path, the pendulum would raise one wing and lower the other, and thereby straighten the machine's path. The first flight test indicated that such a device could work, but that lateral instability would have to be much less than that exhibited by

iv

Renard's machine to be really successful! Apart from the pendulum, the stabilising properties of a gyroscope were also considered, and a noteworthy 'first' in this connection was the stabiliser patented in 1891 by Sir Hiram Maxim and installed in his steam-powered machine. The design concept was somewhat ahead of its time in that it also comprised a servo control loop and other features which are basic to today's automatic flight control systems. Maxim's flying machine unfortunately, came to an untimely end before the stabiliser could be tested under 'live' conditions.

When later pioneers took up the challenge of designing machines in which they themselves ventured to fly, the possibility of manoeuvring their machines away from straight and level flight was realised. However, this was to present another problem; namely, how to cater for the changes in stability which would result when control for initiating a manoeuvre was applied. Thus, 'controllability' was to become an important feature of flying machine design, and one which the Wright brothers were to incorporate in the machine which gained for them the distinction of making that historic flight in 1903. The Wrights' approach to aerodynamic and in-flight problems was more advanced than that of their predecessors, and although the machines built and flown by them were not completely stable, the incorporation of the controllability feature permitted a number of successful flights to be made without artificial stabilisation.

The introduction of control systems by the Wright brothers and subsequent pioneers in their aeroplanes (as they were becoming known) was to establish an additional role for stabilisation devices to play because, if a device could be coupled to the controls, then it alone could correct any departure from a stabilised condition. This was not to go unchallenged of course, and the first practical demonstration of a coupled gyroscopic two-axis control device was given by Lawrence Sperry during his historic flight in Paris in 1914. Thus, it can be said that the foundation for automatically-controlled flight was laid in the early years of this century. By the mid-twenties and in the 'thirties', the development of systems in the United States, the United Kingdom and Europe, became a separate field of engineering technology, and a number of 'automatic pilots' and 'gyropilots' demonstrated their capabilities in commercial and military aircraft operations, and in several historic long-distance record flights. As the technology has continued to develop, system designs have been influenced not only by the advances made in aerodynamics and aircraft controllability characteristics, but also by the advances taking place in other technological fields. For example, the changeover from pneumatic operation of gyroscopes to electrical operation; the processing of control signals by electron tubes and magnetic amplifiers; the introduction of the semi-conductor, and perhaps the greatest influence of all at this moment in time, the vast potential of digital processing technology.

The diversity of present-day automatic flight control systems arises principally because they need tailoring to suit the aerodynamic and flight handling characteristics of individual types of aircraft. It is possible to compromise, and by virtue of this, many of the systems installed in aircraft designed for operation in the general aviation sector are, in fact, highly versatile in their applications; however, there are limitations particularly where the more complex types of transport aircraft are concerned. Thus, any attempts at describing the range of systems and their operating fundamentals would be a mammoth task involving the writing of several volumes. However, any one automatic flight control system may be considered as being composed of four principal elements, which although differing in design and construction, perform functions common to all other control systems. The element functions concerned are progressively: attitude sensing, error signal sensing, signal processing, and conversion of processed signals into powered control, and they set a convenient pattern for a general study of control fundamentals. The material for this book has, therefore, been structured accordingly, and it is hoped that the selected examples of devices performing such functions, will usefully illustrate how relevant principles are applied.

A basic understanding of the principles of flight and aircraft stability, and of servomechanisms, is a pre-requisite to a study of the main subject and they are therefore covered in the opening chapters. With the development of flight director systems and of the concept of integrating basic attitude and navigational data, it became logical to share data and servomechanism links such that a director system could provide guidance commands to an automatic flight control system. Thus, manufacturers develop and make available a wide range of complementary systems, the basic principles of which have also been included in this book. The concluding chapter deals with what may be termed the ultimate in automatic flight control evolution, namely automatic landing.

In preparing the material on systems, I have been greatly assisted by data and illustrations supplied by manufacturers, and would in particular, like to express grateful thanks to Collins Radio Company of England Ltd, Smith's Industries, Marconi Avionics Ltd, and Sperry Rand Ltd, for their permission to use certain of the data, and to have photographs reproduced. My thanks are also extended to friends and colleagues for useful suggestions, comments and assistance in proof reading, and finally to the publisher's editoral staff for their patience.

Copthorne   E.P.
Sussex

1
Principles of Flight

In order to understand the operating fundamentals of any automatic flight control system, it is first necessary to have some understanding of how an aircraft flies, its stability characteristics, and of the conventional means by which it is controlled.

Lift

It is a well-known fact from common experience that all material objects are attracted to the earth by a force which is in proportion to the mass of the object; such a force is called gravity. In order for an object to rise from the earth's surface, and to maintain itself in a continual ascent or at a constant height above the surface, the attraction which gravity has for the object must be opposed by the development of a force called lift. A variety of methods can of course be adopted, the choice being dependent on the object to be lifted. The method with which we are concerned, however, is the one applied to the wings of an aircraft. In this method, wings are designed so that they conform to specific plan forms, and aerofoil-shaped cross-sections, chosen on the basis of size, weight and performance requirements of the particular aircraft. The geometry of some typical wing plan forms, aerofoil cross-sections, and associated terminology are shown in fig. 1.1.

In order to generate the required lifting force there must be relative movement between the wing and the surrounding air. Theoretically, it makes no difference whether air flows over a stationary wing or whether the wing is moved through the air; in practice, however, the latter movement takes place since the wings are carried forward as a result of the propulsive thrust from the aircraft's engine or engines.

Referring to fig. 1.2 it will be noted that when the air strikes the

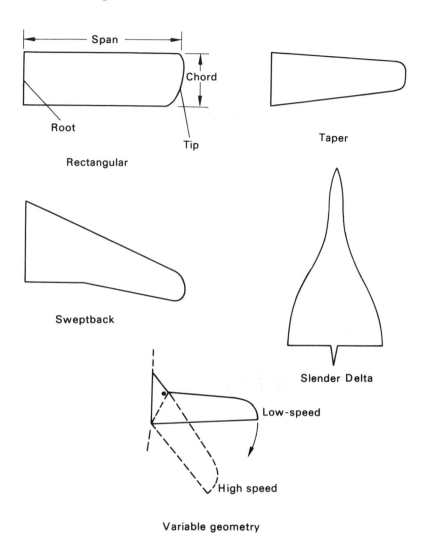

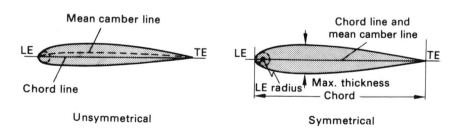

Fig. 1.1 Wing plan-forms and aerofoil terminology

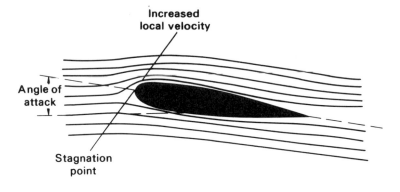

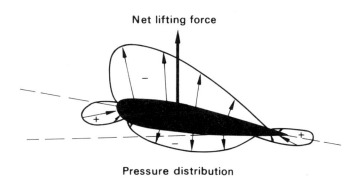

Fig. 1.2 Generation of lift

leading edge of the wing, it divides into a flow over the upper and lower cambered surfaces of its aerofoil section. The mass or continuity of flow is constant, but as a result of differences between the amount of upper and lower surface camber, and also because the wing is at an angle of attack, i.e. at an angle relative to the airflow, the velocity of the airflow over the upper surface will be greater than that of the air flowing along the lower surface. Since the pressure of a fluid (liquid or gas) decreases at points where the velocity of the fluid increases, then for an aircraft wing at small angles of attack the pressures acting on both surfaces of the wing will decrease. However, the decrease is greater on the more highly cambered upper surface, and it is the resulting pressure difference across the wing aerofoil section which generates the net lifting force. The greatest pressures occur at the stagnation point, at points around the leading edge, and at the trailing edge.

3

From the foregoing it is apparent that variations in angle of attack are an important factor in controlling the magnitude of the lift generated by a wing. For example, when angle of attack is increased the velocity of airflow over the upper surface increases at a faster rate than that over the lower surface, thereby changing the pressure distribution such that the net lifting force is further increased. At some critical angle of attack, called the stalling angle, the airflow separates from the upper surface and becomes turbulent, with the result that the lifting force is drastically reduced. In practice, the wings of each type of aircraft are fixed at an optimum angle of the chord line relative to a longitudinal datum (generally called the 'rigging angle of incidence') and the aircraft then flown within a small working range of angles of attack so that in combination the highest lift/drag ratio and economic performance may be obtained.

Other important factors which control pressure distribution and lift are the velocity of the free air flow, its viscosity and its density, the shape and thickness of the aerofoil section adopted for a wing, the wing plan form and its area, and condition of wing surfaces.

Centre of pressure

In connection with the pressure variations occurring across the surfaces of a wing, it is usual to consider the total lift force as acting from one point along the chord line; this point is known as the centre of pressure (CP). As will be noted from fig. 1.3 a, the total lift force is resolved into two principal components: (i) the lift component acting at right angles to the direction of the free airflow, and (ii) a total drag component acting in the direction of the free airflow. The ratio of lift to drag is a measure of the efficiency of any aerofoil section adopted for an aircraft wing.

The location of the CP is a function of camber and the factor known as the lift coefficient, and it varies with the angle of attack. As the angle of attack increases, there is a change in the distribution of pressure above and below the wing such that the magnitude of lift force increases and the CP moves forward. At a certain angle of attack, known as the stalling angle, there is a sudden decrease in the magnitude of the lift force and the CP moves rearward.

Aerodynamic centre

Movement of the CP with changes in angle of attack also causes the pitching moment of a wing to vary, to an extent which depends on the position of the moment reference point 'A'. The pitching moment is equal to the product of the total lift force and the distance from the point 'A' to the CP (fig. 1.3 b). It is, however, possible to locate a reference point about which the pitching moment is constant (C_m) regardless of the angle of attack. Such a point is known as the aerodynamic centre, and for flight at subsonic speeds, it is usually located at or near 25% of the chord. In the mathematical treatment of stability and control of aircraft, allowance is made for the constant pitching moment and it is assumed therefore that the total lift force acts from the aerodynamic centre rather than the CP.

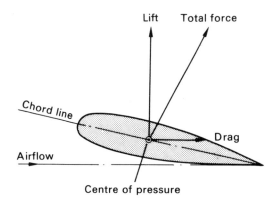

a

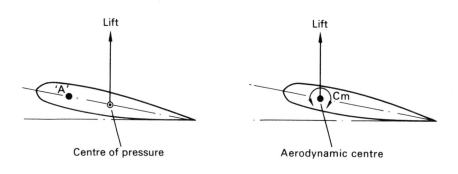

b

Fig. 1.3 Centre of pressure and aerodynamic centre

Drag

The movement of a body through a fluid, whether it is a liquid or air, always produces a force that tends to oppose the movement; such a force is known as drag. Thus the wings of an aircraft, and all its other structural parts exposed to the airflow, experience components of a total drag which must be reduced to a minimum. The drag components arise in several different ways and they can be considered as constituting two principal types of drag, i.e. profile, and induced or vortex; these are summarised in tubular form in fig. 1.4.

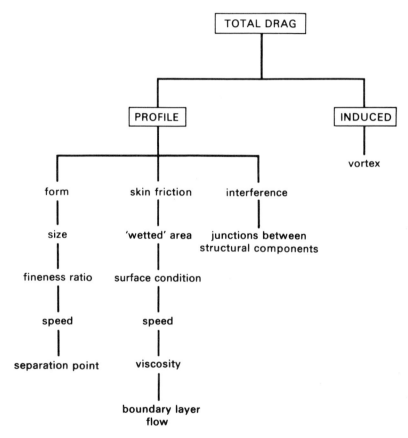

Fig. 1.4 Total drag of an aircraft

Profile drag

Profile drag is composed of the drag components produced by the surface or skin friction created when a body is exposed to airflow, and also by the form or shape of the body. A controlling factor in determining, among other things, the nature of these components, is the very thin layer of air extending from the surface of the body, and referred to as the *boundary layer*. The whole surface area of an aircraft has a boundary layer and therefore has surface friction drag.

If the streamlines of an airflow over the wing of an aircraft are considered as the boundary lines between layers of air, then because air has viscosity, variations in the velocity of each layer will occur as a result of viscous adhesion. Such variations are governed by the distance from the wings' surface, and also by the condition of the surface, i.e. whether it is rough or smooth. The layer adjacent to the surface will adhere to it and so its velocity will approximate to that of the wing. The viscous adhesion between this layer and the one above it will cause the second layer to flow in the direction of wing movement, but at a slightly lower velocity. Similarly, the velocity of the adjacent layers will be lowered until a point is reached where the movement of the wing causes no movement whatsoever of layers of air at some distance 'd' from the wing surface (see fig. 1.5 *a*). Thus, boundary layer may be more closely defined as the layer of air extending from a surface to the point where no viscous drag forces are discernible.

Boundary layer airflow may be either laminar, i.e. streamline, or turbulent as shown in fig. 1.5 *b*. Usually the airflow starts by being laminar over the forward part of the surface, and then at some point, called the *transition point*, the layer tends to break away from the surface and becomes turbulent. The turbulent air mixes with the air above the boundary layer causing a thickening and spreading out of the layer and, as this increases the distance at which viscous drag forces can act, surface friction drag will accordingly increase. Eventually, at a point close to the trailing edge of the wing, the boundary layer separates from the surface resulting in a wake of turbulent air. The separation depends on the rate at which the pressure changes around the body, the rate of pressure change in turn depending on the shape of the body.

The position of the transition point in an airflow of a given density and viscosity depends on the velocity of the airflow and the thickness of the body in the airflow. When applied to a wing of a given thickness, an increase of velocity causes the transition point to move towards the leading edge with the result that more of the wing surface is covered by a turbulent boundary layer and so surface friction drag is further increased. However, a turbulent layer has more kinetic energy than a laminar layer and, since this has the effect of delaying boundary layer separation, the maximum value of lift coefficient is increased.

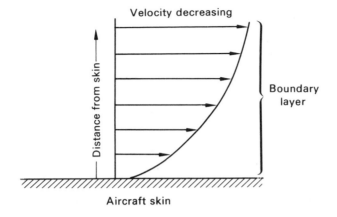

a

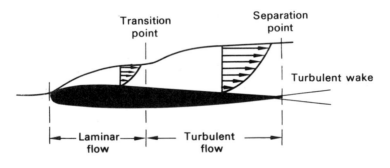

b

Fig. 1.5 Boundary layer

Form drag

This type of drag, as the name suggests, is dependent on the shape of the body exposed to the airflow and as noted earlier, the body shape governs the boundary layer separation and the rate at which the pressure around the body changes. For this reason, therefore, form drag is also referred to as boundary layer normal pressure drag. In order to appreciate the difference between surface friction drag and form drag, let us consider for a moment that the body exposed to the airflow is in the form of a very thin plate. When the plate is at zero angle of attack with respect to the airflow the direction of the airflow will not be materially changed and neither will the velocity or pressure. Thus the boundary layer in this case is purely laminar and the drag results solely from surface friction. When the plate is set at an angle of attack it will cause a change in airflow direction, velocity and pressure, so that the boundary layer now becomes turbulent and begins to separate from the upper surface of the plate. If the angle of attack is further increased such that the total surface area of the plate is presented to the airflow, then there is a complete breakdown of the boundary layer and the drag is wholly form drag.

Interference drag

Interference drag is a result of disturbances to the airflow over an aircraft by the many junctions between major parts of its structure, e.g. between wings and fuselage, engine nacelles and wings. They can all cause changes in the pressure distribution and early separation of the boundary layer.

Induced drag

When a wing is producing lift, the airflow over both the upper and lower surfaces join at the trailing edge, and leave it in the form of a vortex motion the direction of which imparts a downward velocity component to the air. This downwash, as it is called, has the effect of inclining the lift force rearwards so that it will have a component acting in the direction of the drag force. This additional drag component is called the induced or vortex drag, and is affected by such main factors as plan form and aspect ratio of a wing, lift and weight, and speed of the aircraft.

Aircraft stability

Stability is the property of a system whereby the latter returns to a state of equilibrium after it has been displaced from a state of rest or a state of uniform motion. In applying this definition to an aircraft, it can be stated therefore, that following a displacement from an original steady flight path, an aircraft has stability if it returns to that path without movements of its flight control surfaces having to be applied.

In practice however, there are two types of stability to consider: static stability and dynamic stability (see fig. 1.6). Static stability refers to the immediate reaction of the aircraft and its tendency to return to equilibrium after displacement, while dynamic stability refers to the subsequent long-term reaction which is of an oscillatory nature about a neutral or equilibrium position. It is usual to classify both types of

9

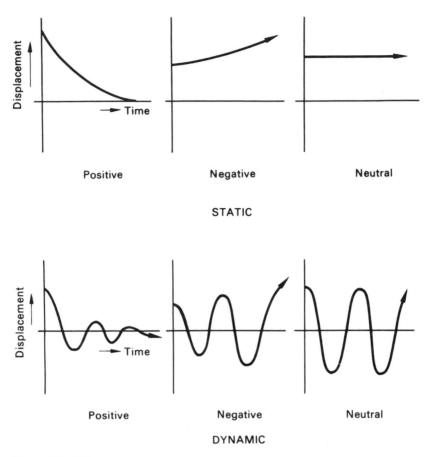

Fig. 1.6 Stability

stability according to the nature of an aircraft's response to displacements from its original steady flight path: thus, stability is *positive* when, subsequent to the displacement, the forces and moments acting on the aircraft return it to its original steady flight path; *neutral* if the forces and moments cause the aircraft to take up a new flight path of constant relationship to the original; and *negative* if the aircraft is caused to diverge from the original steady flight path (an unstable condition). Static stability is a prerequisite for dynamic stability, although the converse is not true; it is possible to have a system which is statically stable, but dynamically unstable.

The displacements of an aircraft which, for example, result from an air disturbance, or by the operation of its flight control system, can take place in any one of three planes; known as the pitching, yawing and rolling planes. This also applies to the aircraft's stabilising motions in

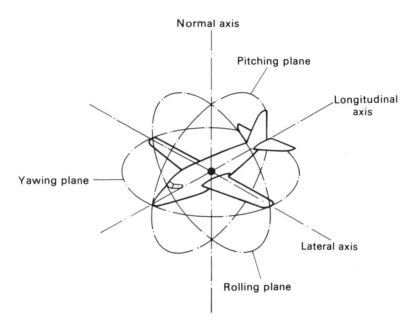

Fig. 1.7 Aircraft axes and displacement planes

response to the displacements. The planes are not constant relative to the earth but, as indicated in fig. 1.7, they are always constant relative to the three body axes passing through the centre of gravity of the aircraft. Both forms of stability relate to the three axes in the following manner: longitudinal stability about the lateral axis, directional or 'weathercock' stability about the normal axis, and lateral stability about the longitudinal axis. In addition to the forces and moments set up by any displacement, forces are also set up as a result of the velocities of motion. These forces are a necessary contribution to the stability of an aircraft, and provide what is termed aerodynamic damping so that motions may be limited or eventually eliminated. The damping in roll, for instance, is the rolling moment due to angular velocity in roll and, since it acts in the opposite sense to the rolling velocity achieved by deflection of the ailerons, the velocity is limited. Damping also applies to pitch and yaw displacements. When this natural form of damping cannot be obtained, it must be furnished by artificial means, e.g. electrically-controlled yaw dampers (see page 177).

Longitudinal stability

Static

When an aircraft has a tendency to return to a trimmed angle of attack position following a displacement, it is said to have positive static longitudinal stability; it thus refers to motion in the pitching plane, and is influenced largely by the design of the horizontal stabiliser, and on the position of the aircraft's centre of gravity under the appropriate flight and load conditions.

The horizontal stabiliser together with the elevators in the neutral or streamlined position form an aerofoil which produces lift at varying angles of attack, the lift in turn producing either an upward or downward restoring moment to balance wing pitching moments about the aircraft's centre of gravity. The lift and restoring moments produced are governed by such factors as the area and planform of the stabiliser, the distance of its aerodynamic centre from the centre of gravity, i.e. the moment arm, and also by the effects of airflow downwash from the wings. When the elevators are maintained in the neutral or streamlined position, static stability is referred to as stick-fixed stability, as opposed to stick-free stability which refers to the condition in which the elevators are allowed to float in the airflow, i.e. 'hands-off' flight condition.

Assuming that in the stick-fixed position the aircraft is displaced nose up, the angle of attack of the wings and, therefore, the lift produced, will be temporarily increased by an amount dL, resulting in an increase of the wing pitching moment about the aircraft's centre of gravity. Thus, if the aerodynamic centre is forward of the centre of gravity giving a moment arm of length x as shown at a of fig. 1.8, the wing pitching moment (M_{wp}) is increased by the amount dLx, the nose-up displacement is thereby worsened and the effect is a destabilising one. Since the nose-up displacement lowers the horizontal stabiliser, then its angle of attack and corresponding lift force will also be increased, but as the position of the aerodynamic centre with respect to the aircraft's centre of gravity provides the longer moment arm y, stabiliser lift force produces a stabilising nose-down moment. When the aerodynamic centre of the wings is to the rear of the centre of gravity (fig. 1.8 b) the increase in M_{wp} will be stabilising in its effect so that in conjunction with that produced by the horizontal stabiliser a greater restoring moment is provided.

For a given weight in level flight there is one speed and angle of attack at which an aircraft is in equilibrium, i.e. tail moments equal to wing moments. The speed and angle of attack depend upon the difference in rigging incidence between the chord lines of the wing and horizontal stabiliser; a difference known as the longitudinal dihedral angle. The angle of attack at which equilibrium is obtained is called the *trim point*.

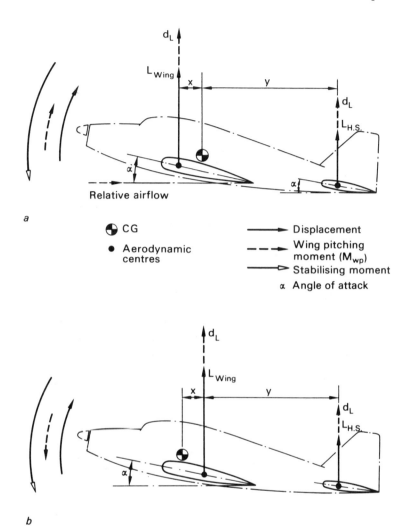

Fig. 1.8 Longitudinal stability

It is thus apparent from fig. 1.8 that the ratio of the wing moment to stabiliser moment, and therefore the degree of longitudinal stability, is affected by the relative positions of both aerodynamic centres, and of centre of gravity. An indication of this is given in fig. 1.9, which is a graphical representation of the conditions appropriate to the wing of an aircraft. Since stability is evidenced by the development of restoring moments, for the wing to contribute to positive static longitudinal stability the aircraft's centre of gravity must be forward of the aerodynamic centre. In this case, the wing contribution is a stable one, and the curve of M_{wp} to lift coefficient (C_L) would have a negative slope

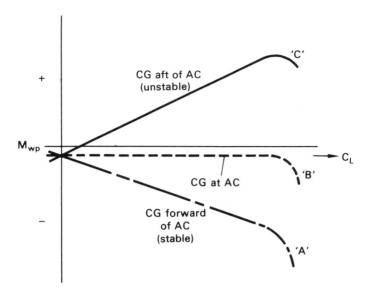

Fig. 1.9 Contribution of wing to longitudinal stability

(curve 'A'). If the centre of gravity were located at the aerodynamic centre, all changes of lift would take place at the centre of gravity and so the wing contribution would be neutral (curve 'B'). An unstable contribution would be made with the centre of gravity to the rear of the aerodynamic centre, and the M_{wp}/C_L curve would then have a positive slope (curve 'C').

In addition to the wings and horizontal stabiliser, other major components of an aircraft such as the fuselage and engine nacelles can also influence the degree of longitudinal stability since, under varying angles of attack, the conditions of airflow and pressure distribution will produce individual pitching moments which can be either stabilising or destabilising in their influence. In plotting the total pitching moments against C_L, and the contribution of the major components to stability, curves similar to those shown in fig. 1.10 *a* are obtained (it is assumed in this example that the centre of gravity is at 30% of the mean aerodynamic chord). The contribution of the wing alone is destabilising as indicated by the positive slope of the curve, an effect which is further increased by the fuselage contribution. The large negative slope of the curve of the horizontal stabiliser contribution indicates its highly stabilising effect, which must be sufficient for the complete aircraft to exhibit positive static stability at the anticipated locations of the centre of gravity.

The typical effect of varying locations of the centre of gravity on static stability is indicated in fig. 1.10 *b*. As the centre of gravity moves

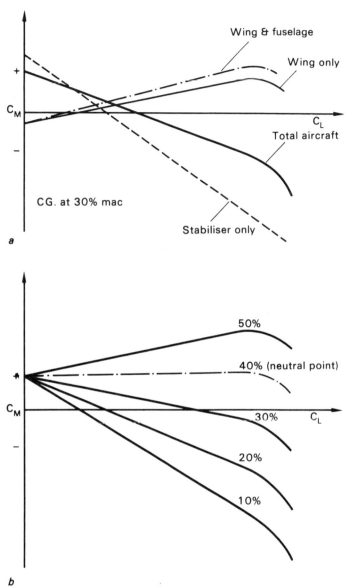

Fig. 1.10 Total pitching moments and effects of varying CG locations

rearward, the static stability decreases, then becomes neutral, and finally results in an unstable condition. The centre of gravity location which produces zero slope and neutral static stability is referred to as the *neutral point*. The distance of the centre of gravity at any time from the neutral point is known as the *static margin* and is an indication of the degree of longitudinal stability. Noticeable changes in static stability

15

can occur at varying values of C_L, particularly when power effects contribute largely to stability, or when significant changes in downwash at the horizontal stabiliser occur. Such changes are illustrated in fig. 1.11. At low values of C_L, the slope of the curve indicates good positive stability, but this gradually starts decreasing with increasing C_L. With continued increase in C_L the slope becomes zero indicating that neutral stability exists. Eventually the slope becomes rapidly positive indicating an unstable 'pitch-up' condition.

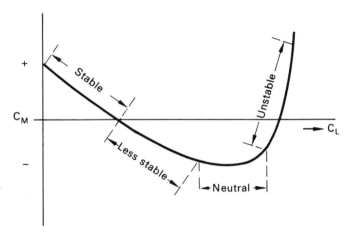

Fig. 1.11 Changes in longitudinal static stability

If the elevators are allowed to float free, they may have a tendency to float or streamline relative to the airflow, when the angle of attack of the horizontal stabiliser is changed. Thus, if the angle of attack is increased and the elevators tend to float up, the change in lift produced by the horizontal stabiliser is less than if the elevator remain fixed; stick-free stability of an aircraft is, therefore, usually less than the stick-fixed stability. Elevators must therefore be properly balanced to reduce floating, and so minimise the differences between stick-fixed and stick-free stability. In the case of fully powered control systems actuated by irreversible mechanisms, the elevators are not free to float and so there is no difference between stick-fixed and stick-free stability.

Dynamic
Longitudinal dynamic stability consists of three basic modes of oscillation, and these are illustrated in fig. 1.12. The first mode (diagram *a*) is of very long period and is referred to as a *phugoid* which involves noticeable variations in pitch attitude, altitude and airspeed. The period of oscillation is quite large, and may be counteracted by very small displacements of the elevator control system. The pitching rate is

low, and as also only negligible changes in angle of attack take place, damping of the phugoid is weak and possibly negative.

The second mode (diagram *b*) is a relatively short period motion that can be assumed to take place with negligible changes in velocity. During the oscillation the aircraft is restored to equilibrium by the

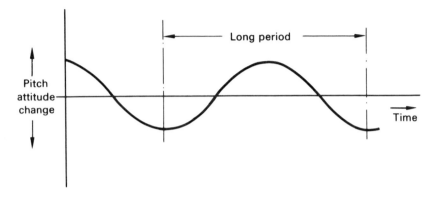

a PHUGOID

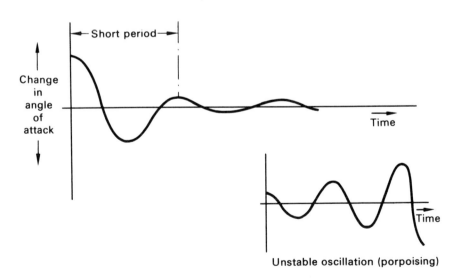

b SHORT PERIOD OSCILLATION

Fig. 1.12 Longitudinal dynamic stability

static stability, and the amplitude of oscillation decreased by pitch damping. If the aircraft has stick-fixed static stability, the pitch damping contributed by the horizontal stabiliser will usually assume sufficient dynamic stability for the short-period oscillation. The second mode, stick-free, has the possibility of weak damping or unstable oscillations, and for this reason elevators must be statically balanced about their hinge line, and aerodynamic control must be within certain limits. If instability were to exist in the second mode, 'porpoising' of the aircraft would result, and because of the short period of oscillation the amplitude can reach dangerous proportions with the possibility of structural damage resulting from the severe flight loads imposed.

The third mode occurs in the stick-free case, and is usually a very short-period oscillation. The motion is essentially one whereby the elevators flap about the hinge line and in most cases the oscillation has very heavy damping.

Directional stability

Directional or 'weathercock' stability involves the development of yawing moments which will oppose displacements about the aircraft's vertical axis and so restore it to equilibrium. Unlike longitudinal stability, however, directional stability is not independent in its influence on the behaviour of an aircraft, because as a result of what is termed aerodynamic coupling effect, yaw displacements and moments also produce roll displacements and moments about the longitudinal axis. Thus, directional motions have an influence on lateral motions and vice versa, the motions involved in each case being yawing, rolling, sideslipping or any combination of these.

As far as yawing displacement, forces, and moments only, are concerned conditions are, in fact, analogous to those relating to longitudinal stability but, whereas in the latter case a horizontal stabiliser has the greatest influence, directional stability is influenced by a vertical stabiliser. This may be seen from diagram a in fig. 1.13.

Assuming that with the rudder in a neutral position the aircraft is yawed to starboard by a disturbance (diagram b), the vertical stabiliser will be at some angle of attack with respect to the airflow and a corresponding side force (lift) will be produced. Since the position of the aerodynamic centre of the stabiliser with respect to the aircraft's centre of gravity provides the longer moment arm, a stabilising yawing moment to port is created and equilibrium is restored. In addition to the stabiliser moment arm, other factors affecting the size of the stabilising moment are the area of the stabiliser, its aerofoil section, angle of attack, aspect ratio and sweepback. As in the case of longitudinal stability other major components of the aircraft can also influence the

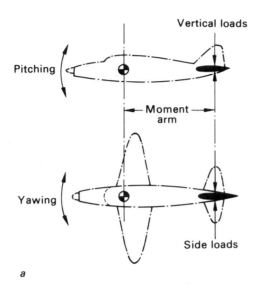

a

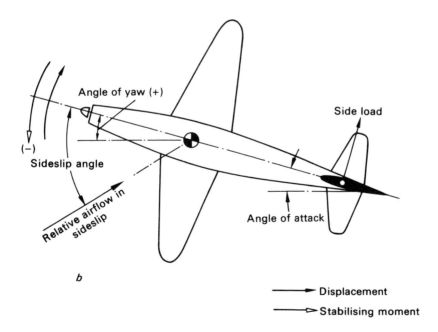

b

Fig. 1.13 Directional stability

degree of directional stability, notably the fuselage and engine nacelles.

When an aircraft is at some angle of yaw, its longitudinal axis is considered as being displaced from a reference azimuth, and by convention, a displacement from this azimuth to starboard constitutes a positive angle of yaw, while a displacement to port constitutes a negative angle of yaw. In the yawed condition, and ignoring aerodynamic cross-coupling, the aircraft is maintaining a forward flight path so that, alternatively, the aircraft can be described as being in a condition of sideslip; thus from the example shown in fig. 1.13 and by convention, an aircraft yawed to starboard is sideslipping to port at a negative angle. The angle of sideslip, therefore, is minus the angle of yaw, and since it relates to the displacement of the aircraft's longitudinal axis from the relative airflow rather than a reference azimuth, it becomes a primary reference in directional stability considerations. This is illustrated graphically in fig. 1.14 a.

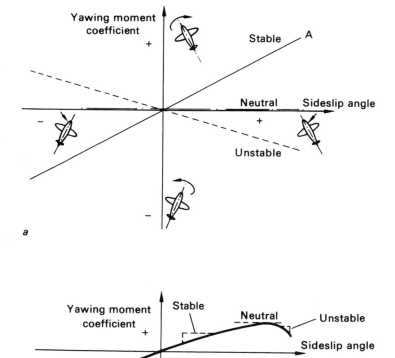

Fig. 1.14 Static directional stability

When an aircraft is subject to a sideslip angle (relative airflow coming from starboard in the case illustrated) static directional stability will be evident if a positive yawing moment coefficient results. Thus, a yawing moment to starboard would be created which tends to 'weathercock' the aircraft into the relative airflow. This is indicated by the positive slope of curve 'A'. If there is zero slope there is of course no tendency to return to equilibrium and so static directional stability is neutral. When the curve has negative slope, the yawing moments developed by sideslip tend to diverge, thereby increasing sideslip such that the aircraft would be directionally unstable.

Diagram *b* serves to illustrate the fact that the instantaneous slope of the curve depicting yawing moment coefficient/sideslip angle will indicate the static directional stability. At small angles of sideslip, a strong positive slope depicts strong directional stability. Large angles produce zero slope and neutral stability; if the sideslip is very high the slope would indicate instability.

Lateral Stability

Static

An aircraft has lateral stability if, following a displacement about the longitudinal axis (called a roll displacement), a rolling moment is produced which will oppose the displacement and return the aircraft to a wings-level condition. In practice however, and because of aerodynamic coupling, rolling moments can also set up yawing or sideslip motions so that the opposing of lateral displacements is not so simple as it seems.

When an aircraft experiences a roll displacement, the effective angle of attack of the down-going wing becomes greater than that of the up-going wing resulting in the appropriate changes in the lift produced (see fig. 1.15). These changes produce a rolling moment which although opposing the initial roll displacement will do no more than provide a damping effect proportional to the rate of displacement. In other words, the aircraft would possess neutral static stability and so would remain in the rolled or banked position. However, the aircraft also experiences a sideslipping motion which is caused by the inclination of the lift vectors at the roll or bank angle. This motion, in turn, causes the airflow to exert forces on the different parts of the aircraft, and it is the rolling moment induced by sideslipping which establishes static stability reaction and return of the aircraft to a wings-level condition. This may be illustrated by a graph of rolling moment coefficient versus sideslip angle such as that shown in fig. 1.16. When the aircraft is subject to a positive sideslip angle, i.e. it sideslips to starboard, positive static stability will be evident if a negative rolling moment to port is

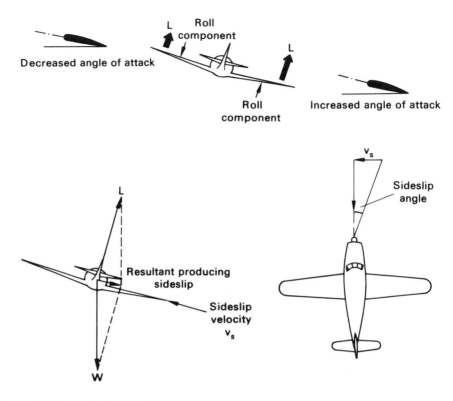

Fig. 1.15 Lateral stability

produced; the curve will have a negative slope (curve 'A'). If the slope of the curve is zero, lateral stability is neutral, while a positive slope indicates lateral instability.

The overall value of the lateral static stability will depend on the effects contributed in varying magnitudes, by each different part of the aircraft, these in turn depending on the configuration of the aircraft and on the condition of flight. The principal contributions to overall lateral static stability are as follows.

1. *The dihedral angle* or upward setting of the wings relative to the horizontal. Dihedral angle is one of the most important contributions to lateral stability which, for this reason, is often referred to as dihedral effect.

2. *The angle at which the wings are swept back* relative to the longitudinal axis. Swept-back wings are a characteristic of many types of high-performance aircraft, producing additional lateral stability which has a greater effect in sideslip at low speeds. In some types of swept-wing aircraft, it may be necessary for stability to be reduced at low speeds,

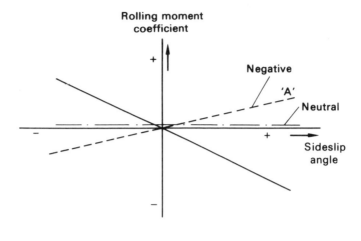

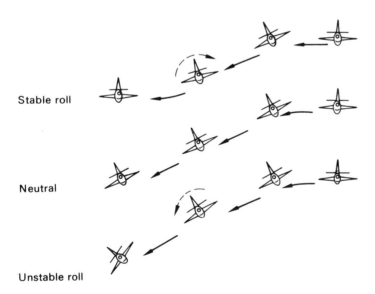

Fig. 1.16 Static lateral stability

and this is done by setting the wings downwards relative to the horizontal, a setting referred to as *anhedral*..

3. *The vertical location of the wings with respect to the fuselage.* In a sideslip, air flows spanwise over the aircraft and causes changes in the effective angle of attack of the wings, such that in the case of a high-wing aircraft,

the rolling moment produced will be a stabilising one, and in the case of a low-wing aircraft a de-stabilising rolling moment will be produced. There is zero effect on lateral stability of an aircraft with wings in the mid-position.

4. *The keel surface.* The side load produced in a sideslip acts on an aircraft's fuselage and on the vertical stabiliser (fin) which together form the keel surface. This side load produces a rolling moment that is generally stabilising, but to a smaller degree than the moments produced in other ways.

5. *The flaps.* When flaps are lowered, they alter the spanwise distribution of pressure and lift, and since they are usually located at the inboard sections of wings, the overall centre of lift is located closer to the fuselage centre line, i.e. the moment arm is reduced. Therefore, any changes of lift resulting from sideslip produce smaller rolling moments thereby reducing the overall lateral stability.

Dynamic
The relative effect of the combined rolling, yawing and sideslip motions produced by aerodynamic coupling, determine the lateral dynamic stability of an aircraft. If the stability characteristics are not satisfactory the complex interaction of the motions will produce three possible forms of dynamic instability: (i) directional divergence, (ii) spiral divergence, and (iii) an oscillatory mode termed Dutch Roll.

Directional divergence

This form of instability is a simple divergence in yaw which may occur if the aircraft is statically unstable about the vertical axis: thus, if the aircraft is flying straight and level and it experiences a small displacement in yaw to port, say, the result will be a yawing moment in the same direction thereby increasing the displacement. In addition, a side force will act on the aircraft in the yawed attitude, so that it will curve away from its original flight path. If the aircraft has lateral static stability directional divergence will occur without any significant degree of bank angle, and the aircraft would still fly a curved path with a very large amount of sideslip.

Spiral divergence

This form of instability exists when the directional static stability is very large compared with lateral stability. Assuming once again that a yaw displacement to port is experienced, because of the greater directional stability the yaw would be quickly eliminated by a stabilising yaw moment set up by the keel surface. A rolling moment to port would also have been set up by the yaw displacement and if it were strong enough to overcome the restoring moment due to lateral stability, and to the damping-in-yaw effect, the angle of bank would increase and cause the aircraft nose to drop into the direction of yawing. The aircraft then begins a nose spiral which gradually increases to a spiral dive.

Dutch roll

This is an oscillatory mode of instability which may occur if the aircraft has positive directional static stability but not so much, in relation to the lateral stability, as may lead to spiral divergence. Dutch roll is commonly found to a varying degree in combinations of high wing loading, sweepback, and high altitude, and where weight is distributed towards wing tips, e.g. engines mounted in pods under the wings. Assuming yet again that the aircraft is yawed to port, it will roll in the same direction. The directional stability will then begin to reduce the yaw to the extent that the aircraft will overswing and start a yaw, and a roll, to starboard. Thus, every period of the continuing oscillations in yaw acts in such a manner as to cause further displacement in roll, the resulting motion being a combination of rolling and yawing oscillations which have the same frequency, but are out of phase with each other.

Controllability

In order for an aircraft to fulfil its intended operational role it must have, in addition to the varying degrees of stability, the ability to respond to requirements for manoeuvring and trimming about its three axes, so that all desired flying attitudes can be achieved and equilibrium be established; in other words, it must have controllability.

Controllability is a different problem from stability in that it requires aerodynamic forces and moments to be produced about the three axes of the aircraft, such forces always opposing the natural stability restoring moments and causing the aircraft to deviate from an equilibrium condition. There is, therefore, a clear relationship between the two which may be illustrated by the analogy of a ball placed on various surfaces (fig. 1.17). Diagram *a* represents the condition of positive static stability and, as we have already learned, any displacement in this condition will always be opposed by a tendency of the ball to return to equilibrium. If, however, it is required to control the ball, and so maintain it in the displaced position, a balancing force must be applied *in the direction* of displacement. When stability is increased a greater balancing force is required to control the ball to the same

25

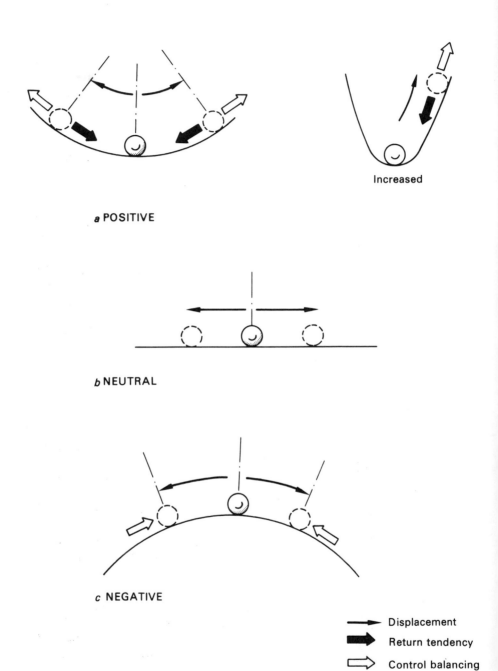

Fig. 1.17 Static stability and controllability

displaced position. A large degree of stability therefore tends to make for less controllability, so that for aircraft it can be stated that the upper limits of its stability are set by the lower limits of controllability.

In a neutrally stable condition (diagram *b*) there is no tendency for the ball to return to equilibrium from a displaced position, and since a new point of equilibrium is always obtained, then no control balancing force is required to maintain the displacement. As the static stability approaches zero, controllability increases to infinity and the only resistance to a displacement would result from damping effects, e.g. the viscosity of air is a damping factor which is proportional to the speed of the displaced body. Thus for an aircraft it can be stated that the lower limits of its stability may be set by the upper limits of controllability.

The effect of negative static stability, i.e. instability, is shown in diagram *c* of fig. 1.17. If the ball is displaced from equilibrium it will tend to continue in the displaced direction and in order to control its displacement a balancing force must, in this case, be applied in a direction *opposite* to the displacement. In applying this reversed form of controllability to an aircraft it would mean that the pilot, in attempting to maintain a state of equilibrium, would also be providing the stability.

It will be apparent from the foregoing that for an aircraft, proper balance must be achieved between stability and controllability, the latter being provided by means of a primary flight control system, and a secondary 'trimming' system.

Primary flight controls

In its basic form, a primary flight control system consists of movable control surfaces connected by cables and rods to cockpit controls which are directly operated by the pilot. The surfaces are aerodynamically balanced to reduce the pilot's physical effort in controlling the aircraft. In high-performance aircraft, the mechanical sections of systems also include powered-actuators (see page 32).

Conventionally there are three sets of control surfaces, and these are situated at the extremities of the wings and stabiliser units (see fig. 1.18) so as to obtain the largest possible controlling moments, consistent with stability, about the three principal axes and centre of gravity. Movement of a control surface causes a change in the aerodynamic profile and therefore a change in the forces produced as shown in fig. 1.19. The pressures acting through the centre of pressure of the control surface, produce a hinge moment which tries to return the surface to its neutral or 'faired' position. The size of the hinge moment is given by the product of the force on the control surface and its distance x from the hinge point. In order to maintain the surface in its

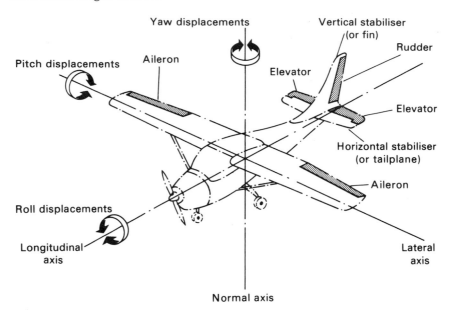

Fig. 1.18 Disposition of flight control surfaces

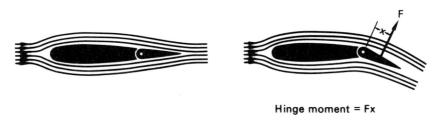

Hinge moment = Fx

Fig. 1.19 Control surface deflection

deflected position, the hinge moment is balanced by a control force applied to the control system either manually or automatically.

It is desirable that each set of control surfaces should produce a moment only about the corresponding axis. In practice, however, the cross-coupling effects, which arise from interaction between directional and lateral stability, apply equally to the flight control system; e.g. a yawing moment in addition to a rolling moment is produced when the ailerons are deflected. This will be described in more detail on page 36.

Ailerons

These provide lateral control, or roll displacements, about the longitudinal axis, the rolling moment produced being opposed by aero-

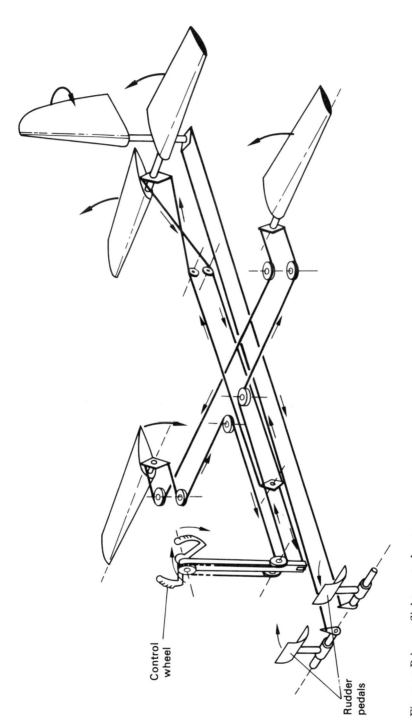

Control
wheel

Rudder
pedals

Fig. 1.20 Primary flight control system

dynamic damping in roll. When the two are in balance the aircraft attains a steady rate of roll; ailerons are therefore essentially rate control devices. As will be noted from fig. 1.20 ailerons are, in most cases, operated by a control 'wheel' pivoted on a control column. They are always connected so that in response to instinctive movements of the control wheel by the pilot, they move in opposite directions thereby assisting each other in producing a roll displacement. Thus, when the control wheel is turned to the left, the left-wing aileron is raised and the wing lifting force is decreased, while the aileron of the right wing is lowered causing the lifting force of that wing to increase and thereby initiate a roll displacement to the left. A similar but opposite effect occurs when the control wheel is turned to the right.

Elevators

Elevators provide longitudinal or pitch control about the lateral axis, and they also assist the horizontal stabiliser to maintain longitudinal stability. Elevators are usually in two separate halves and are normally mounted on a common hinge line at the rear of the horizontal stabiliser. They are connected to the control column, which can be moved backwards and forwards.

When the column is moved backwards, the elevators are raised thereby decreasing the lift of the horizontal stabiliser so that the aircraft is displaced by a pitching moment about the lateral axis into a nose-up, or climbing attitude. Forward movement of the control column lowers the elevators to increase the lift of the horizontal stabiliser and so the pitching moment causes the aircraft to assume a nose-down or descending attitude. Pitch displacements are opposed by aerodynamic damping in pitch and by the longitudinal stability (see page 12) and as the response to elevator deflections is a steady change of attitude, elevators are essentially displacement control devices. It will also be noted from fig. 1.20 that control column and control wheel movements are independent of each other so that lateral and longitudinal displacements can be obtained either separately or in combination.

Rudder

This surface provides yawing moments or directional control about the normal axis of the aircraft, such control being opposed by damping in yaw, and by the directional stability. The rudder is operated in response to instinctive movements by the pilot of a foot-operated rudder bar or, more usually, of a pair of rudder pedals. Thus, if the left pedal is pushed forward the rudder is turned to the left and the force produced on the vertical stabiliser sets up a yawing moment which displaces the aircraft's nose to the left. A corresponding displacement to the right is set up when the right rudder pedal is pushed forward. The response to rudder deflections is a steady state of change of angle of attack on the keel surfaces and so, like the elevators, the rudder is a displacement control device.

Effectiveness of controls

The effectiveness of a control system, i.e. the moment produced for a given control surface deflection, depends on the magnitude of the force produced by the control surface and also on the moment arm, i.e. distance from the centre of gravity. The aerodynamic forces acting on an aircraft depend, among other important factors, on the airstream velocity, so the effectiveness of flight controls varies accordingly. At low speeds, large control surface movements are needed, while smaller ones are necessary at high speeds. Movement of a control surface alone may also alter control effectiveness, since the loads set up tend to twist and bend the aircraft's structure which has a certain amount of inherent flexibility.

In many types of large aircraft it is usual for control surfaces to be arranged in pairs, i.e. an inboard and an outboard aileron on each wing, an inboard and an outboard elevator, and an upper and lower rudder. The reasons for such arrangements are to ensure control effectiveness at low and high speeds, particularly where lateral control is concerned, and also to ensure control in the event of any failures in the system. At low speeds, only the outboard ailerons provide lateral control, while at high speeds they are locked and lateral control is taken over by the inboard ailerons so that the deflecting forces act closer to the longitudinal axis thereby reducing wing twisting. The duplication of elevators and rudder is done primarily as a safety precaution. Each elevator and rudder is operated by an independent control system so that should a failure of a system occur one control surface of a pair can still be effective.

Combined controls

In certain types of aircraft, the primary flight control system is arranged so that one type of control surface may combine its function with that of another; e.g. on a delta wing aircraft such as Concorde, a control surface at each trailing edge can perform the function of both ailerons and elevators; such a control surface is called an *elevon*. When the control column is moved either backwards or forwards both surfaces move together in the manner of elevators, but when the control wheel is turned, one elevon is raised and the other lowered as in the case of conventional ailerons. The interconnection between the two control systems is such that the surfaces can be deflected simultaneously to produce combined pitching and rolling moments.

Another example of combined controls is the one applied to some light aircraft having a 'V' or 'butterfly' tail. In this case, the control surfaces operate as either a rudder or as elevators, and for obvious reasons, they are known as *ruddervators*. They are connected to the control column and are moved up or down to produce pitching moments as in the case of conventional elevators. They are also connected to the rudder pedals, so that they move equal moments in opposite directions to produce the required yawing moment. The control column and rudder pedal systems are connected to the surfaces through a differential linkage or gearing arrangement, so that combined pitching and yawing moments can be obtained.

In some aircraft, elevators are dispensed with and they are substituted with a movable horizontal stabiliser. Thus when the control column is moved the angle of attack of the stabiliser is varied such that a negative angle produces a nose-up attitude, and a positive angle produces a nose-down attitude. Such a stabiliser is known as a *stabilator*.

Powered flight controls

Powered flight controls are employed in high-performance aircraft, and are generally of two main types (i) power-assisted and (ii) power-operated. The choice of either system for a particular type of aircraft is governed by the forces required to overcome the aerodynamic loads acting on the flight control surfaces. In basic form, however, both systems are similar in that a hydraulically-operated servo-control unit, consisting of a control valve and an actuating jack, is connected between the pilot's controls and relevant control surfaces. The major difference, apart from constructional features, is in the method of connecting actuating jacks to control surfaces and this may be seen from fig. 1.21.

In a power-assisted system, the pilot's control is connected to the control surface, e.g. control column to elevators, via a control lever. When the pilot moves the control column to initiate a climb say, the control lever pivots about point 'X', and accordingly commences moving the elevators up. At the same time, the control valve pistons are displaced and this allows oil from the hydraulic system to flow to the left-hand side of the actuating jack piston, the rod of which is secured to the aircraft's structure. The reaction of the pressure exerted on the piston causes the whole servo-unit, and control lever, to move to the left, and because of the greater control effort produced the pilot is assisted in making further upward movement of the elevators.

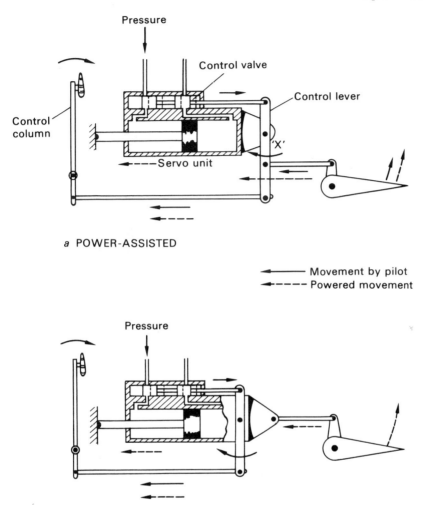

Fig. 1.21 Powered flight controls

In a power-operated system the pilot's control is connected to the control lever only, while the servo-unit is directly connected to the flight control surface. Thus, in the example considered, the effort required by the pilot to move the control column is simply that needed to move the control lever and control valve piston. It does not vary with the effort required to move the control surface which, as will be noted from the diagram, is supplied solely by servo-unit hydraulic power. Since no forces are transmitted back to the pilot he has no 'feel' of the aerodynamic loads acting on the control surfaces. It is necessary

33

therefore, to incorporate an 'artificial feel' device at a point between the pilot's controls, and their connection to the servo-unit control lever.

'Fly-by-wire' system

Another system which may be considered under the heading of powered flight controls, is the one referred to as a 'fly-by-wire' control system. Although not new in concept, complete re-development of the system was seen to be necessary in recent years, as a means of controlling some highly sophisticated types of aircraft coming into service, particularly those designed for military purposes. The problem associated with such aircraft has been one of designing conventional forms of mechanical linkage to suit the complex flight control systems adopted. Thus, a fly-by-wire system, as the name very aptly suggests, is one in which wires carrying electrical signals from the pilot's controls, replace mechanical linkages entirely. In operation, movements of the control column and rudder pedals, and the forces exerted by the pilot, are measured by electrical pick-offs in the cockpit, and the signals produced are then amplified and relayed to operate the hydraulic actuator units which are directly connected to the flight control surfaces.

The first civil aircraft to employ fly-by-wire control is Concorde, but with the difference that a mechanical control linkage is retained only as a standby.

Manoeuvring and forces affecting an aircraft

The displacements resulting from the various movements of the flight control surfaces are those intentionally set up by the pilot in order to manoeuvre his aircraft into required flight attitudes. Such attitudes are: straight and level, climbing, descending, rolling, turning and a combination of these, e.g. a climbing turn. There are four principal forces affecting an aircraft in flight and the directions in which they act are shown in fig. 1.22. Lift, as we learned at the beginning of this chapter, acts at right-angles to the direction of the airflow from the centre of pressure, the position of which can vary with changing angle of attack. Weight acts vertically downward through the centre of gravity which can also vary in position with changing load conditions. Thrust is the forward propulsive force produced by either a turbine engine or a propeller to overcome the opposing total drag force.

Straight and level flight

To be in equilibrium in a straight and level flight attitude at constant

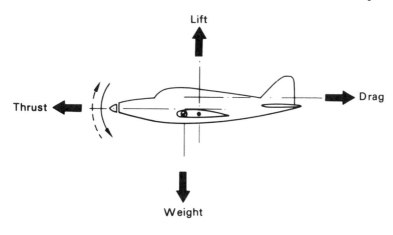

Lift

Drag

Thrust

Weight

⊕ Centre of gravity
• Aerodynamic centre
- - - - ▶ Pitching moment due to thrust/drag couple
———————▶ Pitching moment due to lift/weight couple

Fig. 1.22 Balance of forces

speed, lift must equal weight, and thrust must equal drag, and it is arranged that these forces act from points which are not coincident, thereby producing couples which give rise to pitching moments. For example, because the relative positions of the centre of pressure and centre of gravity can vary during flight, the lift and weight forces produce couples which cause either a nose-up or a nose-down pitching moment. Similarly, pitching moments result from the displacement couples of thrust and drag. Ideally, the moments arising from these two couples should balance each other, and by design it is usual for a nose-down moment due to the lift/weight couple, to be balanced by a nose-up moment due to the thrust/drag couple as indicated in fig. 1.22. If the thrust is then decreased either by a deliberate reduction in engine power or by an engine failure, the lift/weight couple will overcome the reduced thrust/drag couple and cause a nose-down moment thereby putting the aircraft into a nose-down attitude.

Climbing and descending

These are pitch attitude manoeuvres which are set up by upward and downward movements respectively of the elevators. In the case of stabilators referred to earlier, the horizontal stabiliser is deflected to produce a negative angle of attack for the setting up of a climbing attitude, and a more positive angle of attack for a descending attitude. As an example of how the forces act we may consider the case of an upward deflection of elevators to produce a climbing attitude from straight and level flight as shown in fig. 1.23. When the elevators are deflected a pitching moment is produced to rotate the aircraft about the centre of gravity causing the lift vector to be inclined, and thereby constitute an accelerating force at right angles to the direction of flight causing the aircraft to initially follow a curvilinear path. Diagram *b* is a vectorial representation of the conditions obtaining. The lift force in a climb is normally less than the weight, a component of which acts in the direction of drag; therefore, more power, i.e. greater thrust is required to lift the aircraft at a vertical speed, otherwise known as the rate of climb. At the required rate and angle of climb the elevators are returned to their neutral position, as at point A, and the aircraft will fly along a path tangential to the original curve.

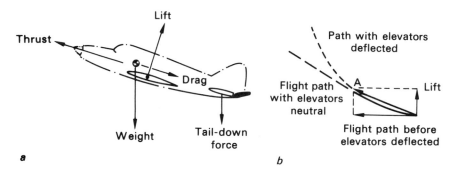

Fig. 1.23 Climbing

Rolling and turning

Rolling of an aircraft takes place about the longitudinal axis, and is initiated by deflecting the ailerons in the required direction. As the effective angle of attack of each wing is thereby changed, then the down-going wing produces a greater lift than the up-going wing (see page 21) and so a rolling moment is established. The total lift vector (see fig. 1.24) rotates through the same angle as the aircraft and gives rise to two components, one vertical and equal to $L \cos \theta$ and the other horizontal and equal to $L \sin \theta$. The latter component acts through the centre of gravity, and it establishes an inwards or centripetal force, thereby causing the aircraft to accelerate into a curvilinear flight path; thus displacing an aircraft into a rolled attitude also results in turning.

For any given airspeed and turn radius, however, turning of this nature would only occur at one correct angle of bank. At any other angle, and because of a cross-coupling response (see page 28), a yawing

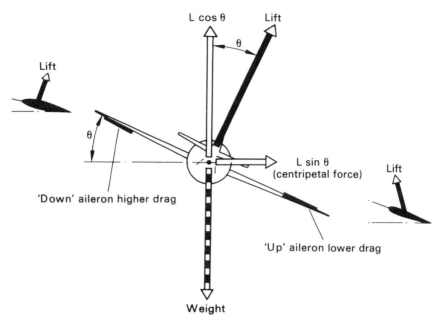

Fig. 1.24 Rolling and turning

moment is produced which opposes the rolling moment. The yawing moment arises in this case, because the lift vector of the down-going wing is inclined forwards, while that on the up-going wing is inclined rearward. Furthermore, the up-going wing being further from the centre of the turn, has the greater angular velocity, and so it sustains more drag. The ailerons themselves, when in their deflected positions, can also create yaw (adverse aileron yaw) their effect being to alter the wing drag. This effect is reduced as much as possible by employing such methods as differential aileron deflection or in some cases by coupling the aileron control system to that of the rudder.

A yawing moment also results in sideslip (see also page 20) and this must be prevented if the aircraft is to be manoeuvred into a steady turn at any speed and roll angle; in other words, the turn must be a co-ordinated one. If an aircraft has a well-designed aileron system, a co-ordinated turn can be achieved by aileron deflection alone. As is more often the case however, the ailerons must be assisted by deflection of the rudder in the direction of its turn, thereby creating a side force on the vertical stabiliser to overcome adverse aileron yaw.

Trimming

The balancing of the aerodynamic forces and moments and the

37

establishment of desired flight attitudes are continuous processes and, as we have already observed, are governed by the degree of inherent stability of an aircraft and by the manoeuvring capability afforded by its primary flight control system. In flight, however, control must also be exercised over changes in weight and centre of gravity locations which occur as a result of the consumption of fuel, disposition of passengers and cargo, flight under asymmetric power conditions, etc; in addition, the attitude changes resulting from the lowering of flaps must also be controlled. Although the required control could be maintained by repositioning the relevant primary flight control surfaces, varying degrees of physical effort on the part of a pilot would be needed to keep the control surfaces in specifically displaced positions. It is usual, therefore, to provide a secondary control system which can be separately adjusted so that it will displace the primary control surfaces, thereby reducing the effects of aerodynamic loads on the primary control system, and so relieving the pilot of undue physical effort. The operation of such a system is referred to as 'trimming', and some typical methods by which it is operated are described briefly in the following paragraphs.

Trim tabs

In this method, which may be considered as the basic form of trimming, an auxiliary surface known as a tab is hinged at the trailing edge of a primary control surface and is connected via a cable, linkage and gearing system to a trim wheel in the cockpit. The wheel is arranged so that it can be rotated in the same sense as the required trim change.

As an example of tab operation, let us consider the case whereby balancing of forces and moments to maintain straight and level flight requires that the aircraft adopt a nose-up attitude. In order to obtain this the elevators must be displaced in an upward position, but for this to be done by movement of the control column the pilot would have to maintain a constant pull on the control column. However, by means of an elevator trim tab, the pilot can set-up the required elevator displacement simply by rotating the trim wheel in the appropriate direction, in this case rearwards. As will be noted from fig. 1.25, the tab will move downwards, so that it is the airloads acting on the tab which will deflect the elevators upwards, and also move the control column to some rearward position. In terms of moments, the one produced by the elevators is $F_1 \times a$, and this is balanced by that produced by the tab, i.e. $F_2 \times b$.

Tabs may also be designed for purposes other than trimming, depending on the aerodynamic and flight control system characteristics appropriate to a particular type of aircraft. For example, they may be

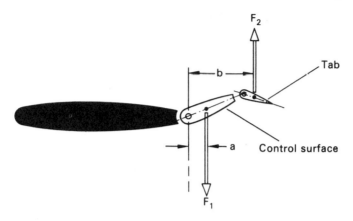

Fig. 1.25 Principle of a trim tab

designed for (i) balancing the flight controls by varying the hinge moments produced by the controls; these are known as balance or geared tabs, (ii) reducing control loads at high speeds (spring tabs), and (iii) reducing control loads necessary to manoeuvre an aircraft (servo tabs).

All-moving tail

On many high-performance aircraft, trimming is effected by varying the angle of incidence of the horizontal stabiliser, the latter also operating in conjunction with elevators. This provides a much wider range of trim capability, and more precise manoeuvring in the pitching plane is possible because the full range of elevator movement is always available. Furthermore, this all-moving tail configuration overcomes the loss of effectiveness from which the use of elevators alone can suffer, especially at high speeds.

It is beyond the scope of this book to go into any detail relating to all of the various methods of stabiliser operation, but the one adopted for the Boeing 707 serves as a useful example of the fundamental principles involved (see fig. 1.26). The incidence of the stabiliser is varied by an actuator assembly which can be operated by any one of three methods: (i) by energising an electric actuator motor through switches on the control columns; (ii) by a trim servomotor (see page 173) which responds to signals from the automatic flight control system; if the latter is not in control, the servomotor can also respond to signals from a Mach trim system (see page 189), and (iii) by manually-operated trim wheels and control cables; this method is for emergency operation in the event of malfunction of the other two methods.

The actuator assembly consists of a jackscrew on which is threaded

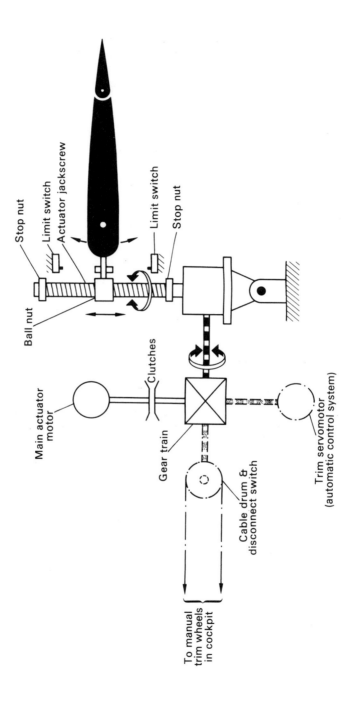

Fig. 1.26 Stabiliser trim system

a ball nut connected to the leading edge section of the horizontal stabiliser. The lower portion of the assembly is connected to the fuselage structure by a gimbal which allows fore and aft angular movement of the actuator during stabiliser positioning. Similarly, the ball nut operates in a gimbal to prevent binding of the jackscrew. The operating range of the ball nut, and stabiliser movement, is limited by stop nuts at each end of the jackscrew.

The primary method of rotating the jackscrew is by means of a 115-volt three-phase motor connected to gearing which also forms part of the actuator. When the motor is energised via the control column switches, it rotates in one direction only, and its drive is transmitted to the jackscrew through either one of two electro-magnetic clutches which, on being energised, permit jackscrew rotation in either direction, corresponding to 'nose-up' or 'nose-down' trim. To prevent the stabiliser from being motor-driven onto either of the stop nuts, limit switches are provided, and on being mechanically operated by a striker on the stabiliser they de-energise the appropriate electro-magnetic clutch circuit. In the event that the actuator ball nut is driven onto either of the stops, a mechanical torque limiter is operated to prevent damage being done to the jackscrew actuator. When the trim system is not in operation, rotation of the jackscrew under the influence of air loads acting on the stabiliser is prevented by a braking system.

In the event of malfunction of the main actuator motor system, or of the automatic trim servomotor system, trimming may be carried out manually by means of trim wheels in the cockpit, and by cables connected to a cable drum and a disconnect clutch.

The elevators provide for the control of manoeuvres in the pitching planes with the stabiliser in a trimmed position. In operation, however, they differ from the more conventional elevator systems in that they can be deflected not only directly from the control columns but also by aerodynamic loads acting on control tabs at the trailing edges of the elevators; the relevant control action depends on whether the aircraft is flying at either low speed or high speed. Deflection of the tabs themselves is also initiated by movement of the control columns. The mechanical arrangement adopted is schematically indicated in fig. 1.27, and for the purpose of explaining its operation it is assumed that a climbing attitude is to be originated.

When the necessary pull force is exerted on the control column, the mechanical linkage to the elevators moves a pivoted follow-up crank and this, in turn, deflects the tab downwards. Thus, an air load can start acting on the tab to assist in deflecting the elevators upward. At low speeds, the aerodynamic load is correspondingly low and, as this requires a greater deflection of the elevators, the design of the system enables the pilot to move the elevator directly from the control column.

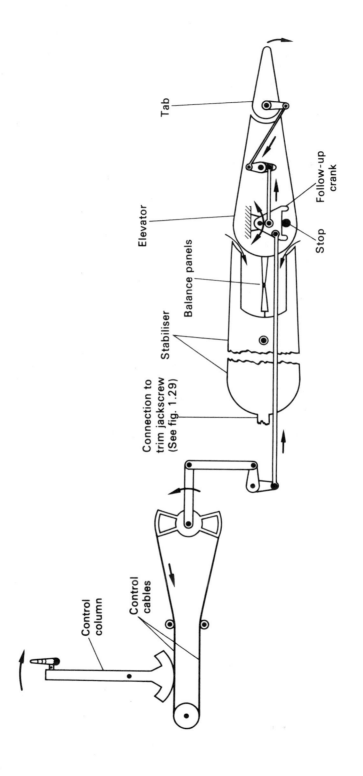

Fig. 1.27 Elevator control (all-moving tail)

This is accomplished by means of the follow-up crank which, as will be noted from fig. 1.27, is provided with a pawl that comes into contact with a stop on the elevator structure. Further movement of the tab is provided by the linkage from the follow-up crank. Deflection of the elevators for originating a descending attitude is obtained when the second pawl comes into contact with the stop. When the aircraft is on the ground the elevators are also deflected by this direct control method.

Under high speed conditions, the aerodynamic load is correspondingly greater and, as smaller deflections of the elevators are required for changing the pitch attitude, the tab alone can assume elevator control without the follow-up crank having to make contact with the stop on the elevator structure.

It will also be noted from fig. 1.27 that the leading edge of an elevator is projected forward through vented gaps in the rear of the stabiliser and is hinge-connected to a balance panel enclosed in a separate bay within the stabiliser. Balance panels and bays are provided at several points for each elevator. The balance panels serve a two-fold purpose: (i) to statically balance the elevators about their hinge centres lines, and (ii) under the influence of aerodynamic loads to further assist in elevator movement.

When the elevators are deflected, the projections and balance panels are moved about their hinge points, thereby varying the sizes of the upper and lower vent gaps. Thus, under the conditions of attitude change considered as an example, the projections and balance panels move downwards to cause an increase in the size of the upper vent gap. This results in the air pressure above the balance panels becoming greater than that below them, so holding the panels down and thereby assisting the elevator control tab to maintain the deflected position of the elevator.

Flying tail

A flying tail is one which controls both manoeuvring in the pitching plane, and trimming, by means of a variable-incidence stabiliser. Elevators are also provided but they can only be operated by direct movement of the stabiliser itself, thereby supplementing its control functions rather than serving as an independent pitch manoeuvring control surface. The one employed on H.S. Trident aircraft serves as an example and its mechanical arrangement and operation under climb conditions are schematically illustrated in fig. 1.28.

Stabiliser incidence is varied either by appropriate movements of the control column, or by rotation of a pitch trim wheel. In each case, movements are finally transmitted via a common differential unit and a hydraulic power-assisted servomotor and actuator jack. The function

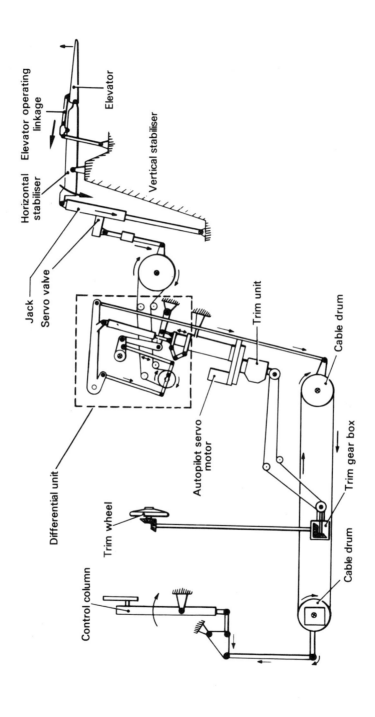

Fig. 1.28 Flying tail

of the differential unit is to vary the final control drive such that the trim control moves the stabiliser through a greater incidence range than that obtainable from the control column. When the autopilot is in control, stabiliser incidence is varied by a servomotor which, as can be seen from fig. 1.28, is connected to the pitch trim control system.

Mach trim

In aircraft which are capable of flying at high subsonic speeds, and of transition to supersonic speed, larger than normal rearward movements of the wing centre of pressure occur and in consequence larger nose-down pitching moments are produced; the attitude change being generally referred to as 'tuck under'. The attitude change is, of course, corrected and trimmed out by designing such aircraft so that they have the essential stability characteristics and trimming method, e.g. the variable incidence horizontal stabiliser already referred to. However, at a certain ratio of aircraft speed to the local speed of sound, or Mach number as it is called, compressibility effects arise which make the counteracting nose-up pitching moment produced by trimming the horizontal stabiliser to a negative angle of attack position, less effective as aircraft speed increases. Under manually controlled flight conditions, this would necessitate the pilot having to make prolonged trim changes

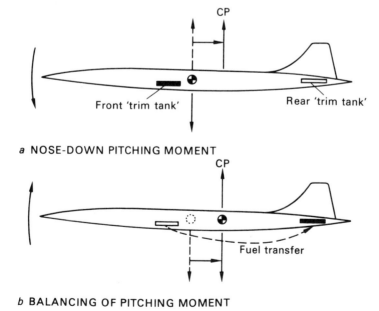

a NOSE-DOWN PITCHING MOMENT

b BALANCING OF PITCHING MOMENT

Fig. 1.29 Mach trimming

45

and to hold higher forces on the control column when displacing the elevators relative to a specific trimmed condition. It is usual therefore to install what is termed a Mach trim system (see also page 189) which automatically senses increases of speed above the appropriate datum Mach number and, by means of servo coupling, automatically re-adjusts the position of the horizontal stabiliser thereby maintaining the pitch trim of the aircraft.

Another example of Mach trimming is the one adopted for 'Concorde' and shown schematically in fig. 1.29. During transition from subsonic to supersonic speed, the nose-down pitching moment (diagram *a*) is counteracted by transferring fuel from a front 'trim tank' to a rear 'trim tank' so that the centre of gravity is moved rearwards thereby removing the couple introduced by the movement of the centre of pressure (diagram *b*).

Direct lift control (DLC)

In a conventional fixed wing aircraft, and as we have already noted, vertical speed is controlled in the long term by engine power, and in the short term by the pitching moment i.e. by the elevators. Elevator control, however, has three principal drawbacks: (i) it implies a lag in operation, the lag increasing with aircraft size and inertia, (ii) changes in altitude are inevitable in controlling vertical speed, and (iii) the initial response is in the reverse direction. For very large aircraft therefore, and those which require close monitoring of both altitude and rate of descent, elevator control of vertical speed may be undesirable.

A system of direct lift control (DLC) is therefore adopted in several types of large aircraft (the DC-10 and the Tristar are two examples) and is one which produces lift forces in the direction a pilot desires to move the aircraft without any of the above drawbacks. This is accomplished by moving an auxiliary lift surface(s) such as biased spoilers, in addition to the elevators. Additional DLC benefits include reduction in normal acceleration of the aircraft's centre of gravity, improved handling in turbulence, and reduction in cockpit workload.

DLC systems can be either 'blended', i.e. they respond to normal fore and aft movements of a control column, or they may be controlled by a separate control device. They can be open-loop with a fixed ratio interconnect between the elevators and DLC surface or closed-loop with feedbacks of pitch angle, pitch rate, pitch acceleration, and/or normal acceleration.

2
Servomechanisms and Automatic Control Fundamentals

In manually controlled flight, the pilot and the flight control system of his aircraft together comprise what may be termed a closed-loop servo-system. Let us consider the simple case of an aircraft which after flying on a constant heading at a particular altitude is required to continue its flight on the same constant heading, but at a lower altitude. The pilot will move the control column forward to apply downward movement to the elevators, thus causing a nose-down attitude of the aircraft and initiation of the descent. Since the descent must be made at a certain angle and rate of change the pilot will also monitor those of his primary flight instruments which detect and indicate attitude changes; namely, gyro horizon, vertical speed indicator, altimeter and airspeed indicator, and then start returning the elevators to their neutral position by pulling back on the control column. In order to level out at the new altitude, the control column will firstly be pulled further back, thereby applying upward movement of the elevators to produce a nose-up attitude of the aircraft, and then will be moved forward again to position the elevators in neutral to fly into the new level flight attitude.

From the foregoing, and much simplified, explanation of how an attitude change is effected, the particular point to be noted is that a pilot must always 'follow-up' his initial control inputs by applying secondary opposing inputs, thereby progressively removing control so that the attitude changes will be made as smoothly and as accurately as possible, and without exceeding those changes demanded by the input. Such a closed-loop servomechanism technique is applied to automatic flight control systems, the 'follow-up' action in this connection being referred to as 'feedback'.

Servomechanisms

A servomechanism may be broadly defined as a closed-loop control system in which a small power input controls a much larger power output in a strictly proportionate manner. In applying such a mechanism to the automatic control of an aircraft, the system must be capable of continuous operation and have the ability to (i) detect the difference between an input and an output (error detection); (ii) amplify the error signals; and (iii) control the closing of the servo loop by providing the feedback.

There are two main classes of servomechanism: (i) position control and (ii) speed control; both classes may be independently applied to automatic flight control systems depending respectively on whether they are of the displacement type or the rate sensing type. In some control systems they may also be used in conjunction with each other.

Position control servomechanism

A block schematic diagram of a position control servomechanism is illustrated in fig. 2.1, and from this it will be noted that it is one in which a load has to be rotated through an output angle θ_o corresponding

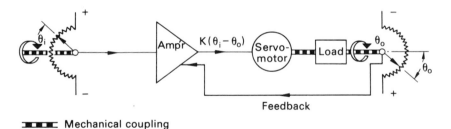

Fig. 2.1 Position control servomechanism

to an input angle θ_i of a controlling shaft. The controlling shaft is, in this example, mechanically coupled to the wiper arm of a potentiometer, the signal output of which is fed to a servomotor via an amplifier. The output angle of the load is measured by a second potentiometer whose wiper arm is mechanically coupled to an output shaft. The potentiometers are electrically connected such that when their wiper arms occupy corresponding angular positions the servomechanism is in a 'null' or zero signal condition. When it is required to move the load to a particular angular position (θ_o) the controlling shaft is rotated through the appropriate number of degrees; thus the mechanism is no longer at 'null' and an error signal corresponding to angle θ_i is produced and fed to the amplifier. The amplifier has an amplification factor of K, and therefore the input to the servomotor is increased to $K\theta_i$. As the motor positions the load, the output shaft rotates the wiper arm of the second potentiometer to produce a signal corresponding to an angle θ_o. This signal is fed back to the amplifier thereby reducing the input error signal to the amplifier so that the real output from this unit to the servomotor is $K(\theta_i-\theta_o)$. When the load finally reaches the position required, the servomechanism will then be at a new 'null' condition.

Speed control servomechanism

A speed control servomechanism is one in which error signals are produced as a result of a difference between voltages corresponding to input and output speeds, such signals being used to control the speed of the servomotor and load. Referring to fig. 2.2, it will be noted that

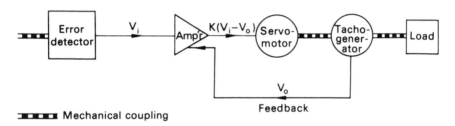

Mechanical coupling

Fig. 2.2 Speed control servomechanism

the system differs from that used for position control in that the servomotor also drives a device known as a tachogenerator. When it is required to operate the load, the servomotor is driven by an amplified input error voltage, V_i, and the motor accelerates the load towards the required speed. At the same time, the motor drives the tachogenerator which produces an output voltage, V_o, in proportion to its speed of rotation. The output voltage is fed back to the amplifier thereby reducing the input error voltage and so producing a real output from the amplifier equal to $K(V_i-V_o)$. The servomotor in this class of servomechanism (sometimes called a velodyne) is therefore controlled by differences in voltages, and will speed up or slow down until the difference is zero.

Response of servomechanisms

The response of a servomechanism is the pattern of behaviour of the load when a change is made to the input condition, the most important factors being the form which the input change takes and the various restraints, friction, etc., which act on the output. There are two types of input change to be considered and these are referred to as step input, and ramp input, the names being derived from the shape of the curves of input against time as shown in fig. 2.3.

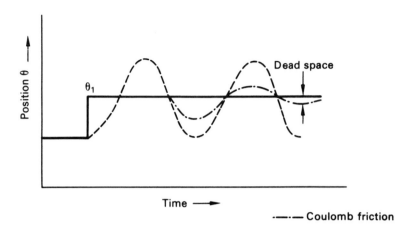

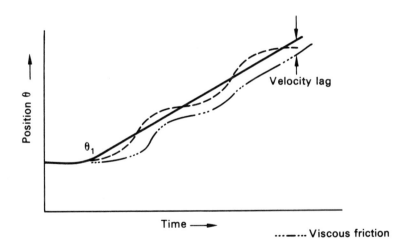

Fig. 2.3 Response of servomechanisms   *a* Step input   *b* Ramp input

A *step input* is one whereby the input (e.g. the controlling shaft of the system shown in fig. 2.1) is suddenly changed to a new angular position θ_i from a null position. Because of the inertia of the load an angular change at the servomechanism output will not be able to follow exactly that at the input, with the result that a large error signal is produced initially. This causes the load to be accelerated to its required position, and thereby reduces the error to zero. At this point however, and although the acceleration is zero, the load has reached a steady rate of change, and so it overshoots resulting in an increase of error in the opposite sense to decelerate the load until it comes to rest in the opposite direction. By this time the error signal is equal to the original error signal but of opposite polarity, and so the load is accelerated back towards the required position and produces another overshoot. If the frictional losses in the system are negligible, a continuous oscillation is produced.

A *ramp input* is one whereby the input is suddenly moved at a constant speed. In the early stages of the input, and while the error signal is small, the load accelerates slowly and lags behind the input. The signal increases as the lag increases, thereby building up the acceleration. Eventually the input and load speeds are equal, but since a substantial position error exists, the load continues to accelerate, the acceleration is reduced, and the load attains a constant speed at zero position error with no error signal. Thus, as in the case of a step input, a continuous oscillation is produced.

Damping

Oscillatory responses of a servomechanism from whatever cause are obviously undesirable, and so it is necessary to provide some form of damping by which a load can be brought to rest in its required position with the minimum of overshoot. Servomechanisms possess various inherent factors which, together, have the general effect of reducing the amplitude of each successive oscillation; such factors include static friction, kinetic friction, eddy current, lubricant viscosity, etc., and while contributing to damping requirements they do have certain detrimental effects, e.g. power is wasted, and errors can be introduced with the servomechanism operating in the steady state. The effects are partly due to a small force of constant magnitude known as *coulomb friction*, and to *viscous friction* which increases with speed.

Coulomb friction relates particularly to the response to a step input and this is illustrated in *a* of fig. 2.3. It has the tendency to downgrade the sensitivity of a servomechanism, since the torque required to overcome the friction must be generated before any movement of the load takes place. To provide this torque the load error must reach some finite size and any errors less than this will not be corrected. The load comes to rest somewhere within a band of error (the dead space), the width of the band depending on the amount of coulomb friction. The friction is, however, very small in most current types of servomechanism so that its effect can be neglected.

Viscous friction (fig. 2.3 *b*) produces a similar dead space effect, but as the friction varies with speed, the effect is associated with a ramp input. In the steady state the load moves with constant speed, and is therefore resisted by viscous friction. An error signal must be produced to overcome this and so a steady state error must exist, the error being known as *velocity lag*. Coulomb friction also contributes to velocity lag, but it is considered small in comparison with viscous friction.

The transient responses just described are generally adequate in applications requiring the use of small position servomechanisms, but when large loads are involved it is desirable to further reduce the number of oscillations, and the response time. Two methods commonly employed are *viscous damping* and *velocity feedback* damping.

Viscous damping

A device commonly used for viscous damping is one in which a disc is free to rotate between the pole faces of an electromagnet. The disc is coupled to the servomechanism output shaft so that, as it rotates, eddy currents are induced in the disc. The eddy currents are of a magnitude proportional to the field strength, and to the disc velocity, and they establish magnetic fields and forces which oppose rotation of the disc and output shaft. The damping effect is produced by absorption of the servomotor torque in the desired proportion.

The response achieved by additional viscous damping can be made adequate for the particular servomechanism function, but since it absorbs servomotor torque it has the disadvantage of wasting energy; furthermore, where a ramp input is concerned the velocity lag is increased.

Velocity feedback damping

Velocity feedback damping overcomes the wasting of energy by feeding back a voltage from a tachogenerator, the voltage being proportional to the load velocity and in opposition to the error signal applied to the amplifier unit of the servomechanism. Thus, the net input to the amplifier is the error signal voltage (i.e. the difference between input and output voltages) minus the velocity feedback voltage and since the overall effect will result in a lowering of the amplifier output, the servomotor torque will also be lowered so that less energy will be expended. Velocity feedback also increases velocity lag in response to ramp input, but for a different physical reason. In this case, the steady state velocity of the load imposes a signal at the amplifier input which must be cancelled in some way if the steady state velocity is to be maintained. The cancellation can only be made by an equal error signal, which means that an error must exist. By suitably adjusting the feedback voltage it can be arranged that the error signal is reduced to zero and then reversed before the load reaches its new position. In this manner the momentum of the load acting against the reversed servo-motor torque will bring the load to rest just as it reaches its new position, thereby reducing overshoots and subsequent instability.

Error-rate damping

As already noted, in velocity control servomechanisms (ramp input) employing velocity feedback damping the transient response is improved but velocity lag is increased. This can be tolerated in certain applications, but where requirements for rotating a load at constant speed are to be met the lag must be reduced to zero in the steady condition. This may be achieved by adopting either of two methods which in each case produce the same result, i.e. cancelling the velocity feedback signal when the input and output velocities are equal. One method is to fit a second tachogenerator at the input so that it feeds a signal forward into the amplifier, thus making the net input an error voltage plus a voltage proportional to input shaft speed minus the velocity feedback voltage. During a ramp input a steady state is eventually reached in which the tachogenerators apply equal and opposite voltages to the amplifier; the net input is therefore zero. If any velocity lag exists at this stage, the position error signal will establish torques at the servo-motor to reduce it.

The foregoing method, although eliminating velocity lag, presents the difficulty of ensuring that the voltage outputs of both tacho-generators will remain constant over a long period of time. Since the velocity of an error is equal to its rate of change, with respect to time, i.e. the differential of the error, then by combining a differential signal with the actual error signal at the amplifier input, the same final result will be obtained as when using two tachogenerators. In the second method, therefore, the tachogenerators are dispensed with and are replaced by a resistance-capacitance differentiating network.

Transient velocity damping

This type of damping, also known as acceleration feedback, utilises a differentiating network connected in the velocity feedback signal line. Thus, only the derivative of the load velocity reaches the amplifier, with the result that damping is effective only during the transient response period, i.e. when a rate of change of load velocity exists. Once the steady state is reached there is no further rate of change, the derivative is zero, and feedback ceases thereby reducing velocity lag.

Fundamentals of automatic control

Having briefly studied some of the fundamental operating principles of servomechanisms, we can now see how the closed-loop servo technique can be applied as a means of achieving automatic flight control of an aircraft. Fig. 2.4 is a functional diagram of a closed-loop system which is basic to all classes of automatic flight control systems, and from this we note that there are four principal elements which together are allocated the task of coping with what is generally termed 'inner loop stabilisation'. The individual functions of the elements are as follows:

(i) Sensing of attitude changes of the aircraft about its principal axes by means of stable reference devices; e.g. gyroscopes and/or accelerometers;

(ii) Sensing of attitude changes in terms of error signals and the transmission of such signals;

(iii) Processing of error signals and their conversion into a form suitable for operation of the servomotors forming the output stage;

(iv) Conversion of processed signals into movement of the aircraft flight control surfaces.

The number of control loops, or channels, comprising an automatic control system is dependent on the number of axes about which control is to be effected and in this connection it is usual to classify systems in the following manner.

Single-axis in which attitude control is normally about the roll axis only; the control surfaces forming part of the one and only control loop are, therefore, the ailerons. Such a control system is the most basic in concept, and it is used in a number of types of small aircraft for lateral stabilisation, or wing-levelling as it is frequently termed. The pilot can inject command signals into the control loop thereby enabling him to turn the aircraft automatically. In some cases, signals from a compass system and from radio navigation equipment are also injected into the loop so that magnetic headings, and tracking capability can be automatically maintained; such operating modes are known as heading-hold and radio-coupling respectively, and form part of the outer loop control described in chapter 6.

Two-axis in which attitude control is, in most cases, about the roll and pitch axes; the control surfaces forming part of the two loops are, therefore, the ailerons and the elevators. Manual turn control, heading-hold and radio-coupling facilities are normally standard features in any

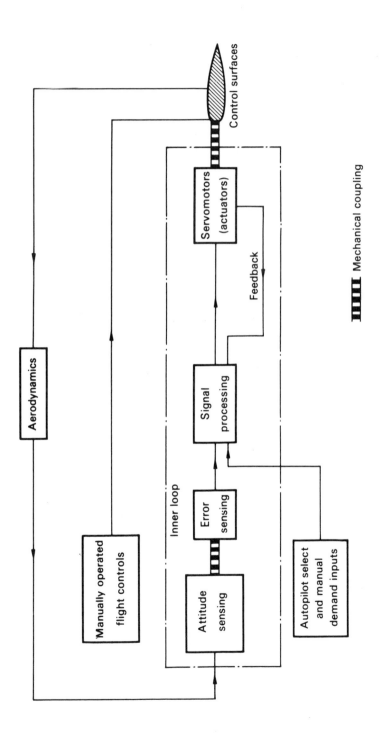

Fig. 2.4 Inner loop stabilisation

one design with, in some cases, an additional facility for selecting and holding a specific altitude (see fig. 2.5).

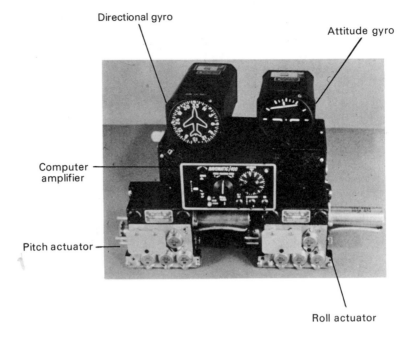

Directional gyro

Attitude gyro

Computer amplifier

Pitch actuator

Roll actuator

Fig. 2.5 Two-axis automatic control system

Three-axis, in which attitude control is about all three axes. These systems are designed to meet the requirements for stabilisation and control of high performance category aircraft, and to have a large number of potential modes of operation (see figs. 2.6 and 2.7).

In its basic mode of operation, the function of an automatic control system is to hold an aircraft on a desired flight path, by detecting and correcting any departure from that path; in other words, its function is one of stabilisation. When a system is initially engaged via appropriate interlock circuits, clutch mechanisms are operated to provide mechanical coupling between the appropriate servomotors and the aircraft's primary flight control system, and the manually trimmed attitude existing at the moment of engagement is maintained.

If the attitude of the aircraft changes as a result of, say, an air disturbance or an out-of-trim condition of the aircraft, the attitude sensing elements will detect this change and their associated signal pick-off elements will translate the change into an error signal. The signal is fed to the relevant control channel amplifier in the signal

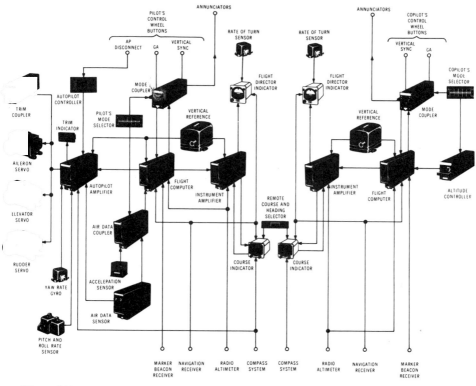

Fig. 2.6 Three-axis automatic control system

processing element and after amplification it is supplied to the servo-motor. For example, if the error signal is caused by a change about the roll axis, the signal is processed by the roll control channel and fed to the roll servomotor which repositions the ailerons to correct the attitude change. The servomotor also repositions a feedback or follow-up element, the purpose of which, as we have already learned from our brief review of servomechanism operation, is to reduce an input error signal and thereby limit the control applied. Thus, the feedback element produces a signal equal and opposite to that of the input error, thereby limiting servomotor operation until it stops with the ailerons in the angular position required to return the aircraft to the level flight attitude. As the aircraft returns, the error signal decreases and the feedback signal, via the amplifier, now causes the servomotor to reduce the angular position of the ailerons towards neutral. A similar sequence takes place when an error signal is caused by a change about either the pitch or yaw axis.

In addition to the foregoing role of inner loop stabilisation, an automatic control system must have the capability of assisting the pilot

57

1. Servomotors
2. Pitch computer
3. Roll computer
4. Yaw computer
5. Gyro unit
6. Trim indicator
7. Mode selector
8. Controller
9. Altitude sensor
10. Airspeed sensor
11. Pitch trim servomotor

Fig. 2.7 Components of a three-axis flight control system

in manoeuvring the aircraft so that its attitude can be changed in order to comply with required in-flight procedures. Such changes would, for example, be a turn on to a new heading, or an altitude change. Any attempt, however, by the pilot to make these changes by applying forces to the control wheel or rudder pedals in the conventional manner would (with the exception of a control wheel steering mode, see page 164) be resisted by the automatic control system since in performing its primary stabilising function it would interpret the changes as disturbances. It is, therefore, necessary to provide a flight control panel through which the pilot can inject command signals into the appropriate control channels and thereby initiate servo-control. The flight control panel may thus be considered as the primary element in the outer control loop (see chapter 6) and the control facilities it provides depend on whether the control system as a whole is a simple single-axis 'wing leveller' or whether it forms part of a more complex flight guidance system. In the basic form, however, all control panels have two main control facilities and these are (i) a turn control, and (ii) a pitch control.

The turn control consists of a control knob which can be displaced to the left or to the right of a neutral position commonly referred to as the 'centre detent' position. When the knob is in this position, the control circuit provides an interlock for pre-selected heading data signals from a compass system. In the displaced position, the interlock circuit is interrupted, and since the control knob is connected to either a potentiometer or a synchro transmitter rotor, depending on the type of control system, a command signal circuit is completed to the roll control channel of the control system and thence to the aileron servomotor. Thus, the aircraft is rolled into a turn at an angle proportional to the amount of displacement of the control knob. The feedback signal generated by servomotor operation opposes the command signal until both signals are equal. In order to maintain the commanded roll angle and turn, the aileron control must be progressively 'taken off'. This is accomplished by the appropriate attitude sensor which, in sensing the roll command as a disturbance, will cause its associated pick-off element to transmit a signal which is ultimately applied to the aileron servomotor causing it to return the ailerons to their neutral positions. The aircraft, therefore, is flown at the required roll angle until the turn control knob is returned to the detent position. When this is done, the roll command signals and the attitude sensor pick-off signals will be in the opposite sense, the ailerons being returned to neutral as the aircraft returns to the level flight attitude. Since the heading data system continuously operates in a follow-up mode, the return of the control knob to detent also permits the signals appropriate to the new heading to be applied to the roll control channel via the re-engaged interlock circuit.

The angle of roll must be limited to angles compatible with the aircraft's control characteristics, and this is effected by passing the command signals through a limiter network. The limiter output is also supplied through a cross-feed circuit to the rudder control channel so that the rudder is displaced by an amount sufficient to provide co-ordination of the turn.

The pitch control comprises a control wheel which can be rotated in a vertical plane, and in the same sense required to establish a nose-down or nose-up displacement from a neutral position. The control wheel is also connected to either a potentiometer, or a synchro transmitter rotor, but in this case, the appropriate command signals are applied to the pitch control channel and elevator servomotor of the control system. Thus, the method of applying control, and of returning the elevators to their neutral position, is similar in operation to that applied to turn control. In systems which incorporate altitude-hold and glide path-coupling facilities (see chapter 6) the pitch control also includes an interlock circuit which disconnects these facilities whenever a pitch attitude change is selected, thereby preventing any opposition to the command signals.

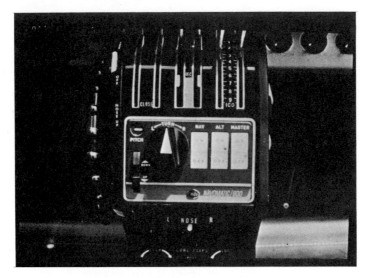

Fig. 2.8 Control panel installed in a small twin-engined aircraft

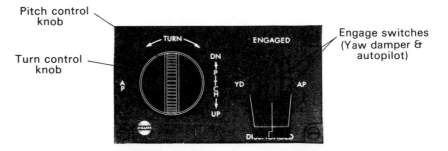

Fig. 2.9 Control panels

Fig. 2.10 Pilot's controller incorporating mode selection facilities

In addition to turn and pitch control facilities, a control panel also incorporates a switch for engaging the servomotors to the aircraft's primary flight control system; two examples are shown in figs. 2.8 and 2.9. In some of the more complex flight guidance systems, it may also be the practice to incorporate all mode selection facilities in a control panel such that it is more appropriate to apply the term 'flight controller'. This may be appreciated by comparing fig. 2.10, which shows the controller of the system employed in Concorde, with the other panels illustrated.

Interlocks

Before an automatic control system can be engaged with an aircraft's flight controls, certain preliminary operating requirements must be fulfilled to ensure that the system is in a condition whereby it may safely take control of the aircraft. The principal requirements are that the connections between system power supplies, the elements comprising the system, and the appropriate signal and engage circuits are electrically complete. It is the practice, therefore, to incorporate within any automatic control system, a series of switches and/or relays, known as interlocks, which operate in a specific sequence to ensure satisfactory engagement, and the coupling of input signals from outer loop control elements (see chapter 6).

The number of interlocks incorporated in any one system varies considerably according to the control capability of that system (see page 54) and space does not permit detailed description of the various functions and circuit combinations. However, the fundamentals of interlock operation in general, may be understood from fig. 2.11 which is a much simplified presentation of an engagement circuit based on that adopted in a current type of automatic control system. It will be noted that the contacts of switches and relays, in the main, form a series-connected circuit, i.e. each must be closed in order to complete the power supply circuits to the servomotor clutches via the engage switch.

When the aircraft's power supply is on, it is automatically supplied to the attitude sensing elements and signal processing elements of the control system, so that they are in a stand-by condition when the engage switch is in the 'off' position. Certain of the relays in the engage circuit are also automatically energised when the power supplies are on, namely, the d.c. and a.c. power monitoring relays and the Mach trim coupler relays. The vertical gyroscope relay also energises automatically but only after the gyroscope has run up to operating speed, and the fast erection cycle has been completed. In order to complete the circuit to the engage switch, the turn control knob must be at its centre detent position, the mode selector knob at the 'manual' position, and as in the example shown, the automatic trim cut-out switch must also be on.

When the engage switch is placed in the 'Autopilot' position, direct current is supplied from the mode selector switch to the engage interlock relay, which on being energised completes the power supply circuit to the elevator and aileron servomotor clutches, and to the coil of an engage relay, which then completes a circuit to the engage switch, the circuit being in parallel with the turn control and mode selector switches. At the same time, of course, the rudder servomotor clutch is energised but in this particular example the circuit is completed via another set of contacts within the engage switch. This also applies to a coil circuit within the engage switch, the purpose of the coil being to hold the switch at the 'Autopilot' engaged position.

As noted earlier (page 59) when it is necessary to apply a turn command to the flight control system, the turn control knob is positioned to the left or right of its detent, and this action corresponds to an 'open interlock' condition. However, as reference to fig. 2.11 will show, this will not cause disengagement of the servomotor clutches, because the engage interlock relay coil then remains energised via the d.c. supply circuit in parallel with the turn control switch. The circuit functions in a similar manner whenever the mode selector switch is positioned out of the 'manual' position in order to apply appropriate outer loop control commands to the flight control system. The circuits relevant to the outer loop elements also incorporate interlocks, and their functions are described in the appropriate sections of this book.

The 'damper' position of the engage switch permits the selection of a

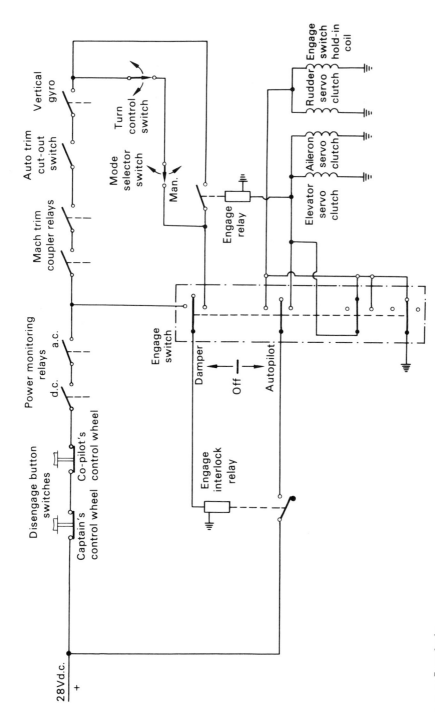

Fig. 2.11 Interlocks

yaw damping facility (page 177) which in the example shown in fig. 2.11, is provided by the rudder servomotor. When selected, the circuits through the turn control and mode selector, together with the aileron and elevator servomotor clutch circuits, are isolated from the engage switch, and the d.c. supply for the rudder servomotor clutch, and engage switch hold-in coil, is fed via the closed contacts of the engage interlock relay.

Disengagement of the automatic control system is normally effected by pressing one or other of the button switches on the control wheels. This action de-energises the engage relay and the engage interlock relay, and also interrupts the engage switch hold-in coil circuit thereby releasing the switch to the 'off' position. Similarly, disengagement will take place whenever any one of the other interlock switches or relays is opened.

Trimming and synchronisation

In addition to the pre-engage requirements that automatic control system circuits are electrically complete, it must also be ensured that on engagement the 'take-over' is effected smoothly, and without 'snatching' of the aircraft's control system. In other words, the aircraft must be trimmed for the desired flight attitude before engagement, and the automatic control system must be synchronised to maintain that attitude on engagement.

When power is applied to the automatic control system, the attitude sensing elements are in operation so that they will always detect the aircraft's attitude, and therefore, supply any necessary control command signals to the servomotors. At the same time, any signals will be supplied to the appropriate channels of a trim indicator (page 187), the pointers of which will be displaced from their central positions thereby indicating the presence of signals at the servomotors, and the direction in which control is required. For example if, before control system engagement, the aircraft is in a climb, or has been trimmed to fly in a nose-up attitude, the pitch attitude sensing element will detect this, and will supply a signal to the elevator servomotor commanding it to rotate in a direction corresponding to 'elevator down', such as would be shown on the trim indicator. Because the signal in this case is a standing one, assuming for the moment that it has no opposition, the servomotor will continue to rotate, and if its clutch was engaged at any one moment the elevators would be snatched from their trimmed position and so cause a nose-down attitude change.

The aerodynamic load acting on the elevators would be felt by the servomotor, thereby helping to retard its rotation. As soon as the sensing element of the pitch attitude detector responds to the attitude change, the opposing signal produced would then eventually stop the motor and rotate it in the opposite direction. Thus, control would be of an oscillatory nature and the aircraft would take up the pitch attitude determined by the attitude detector and not that which it was desired the control system should maintain, i.e. in the example considered a climb or a nose-up trim condition. It is, therefore, necessary to oppose the standing signal and reduce it to zero before engaging the control system, so as to stop the servomotor in a position which is synchronised with the datum attitude detected by the sensing element, such position being indicated by the return of the trim indicator pointer to its central position.

The manner in which synchronising is effected depends on the type of control system. In some cases, usually in some of the more basic types, the pitch control knob on the control panel is manually rotated, thereby injecting an opposing command signal into the amplifier of the elevator channel. In the majority of systems, however, it is effected by means of a synchro transmitter which is coupled to the servomotor output shaft to produce a signal equivalent to the angular position of the shaft. In other words, the synchro forms a position feedback system (see page 177). When used in systems employing rate feedback, the opposing signal is a combination of both position and rate feedback signals.

Although the foregoing description of synchronisation has been related to the pitch channel, it should be noted that the requirements can equally apply to the roll and yaw channels of a control system, the method adopted also varying with the type of system. In one example appropriate to roll channel synchronisation, a filter circuit known as an aileron synchroniser (see fig. 5.1) is used to enable the control system to be engaged during a turn, without incurring a large heading error from the heading existing at the time of engagement. Prior to engagement, the standing signal from the attitude sensing element to the aileron servomotor is fed to the synchroniser and processed so as to cancel the standing signal, and thereby establish a zero bank angle signal as the reference for the attitude sensing element. Upon engagement, the input to the synchroniser is shorted out, and its output falls to zero, leaving a signal output from the sensing element corresponding to zero bank angle. Thus, the servomotor is engaged, without snatching the ailerons, to bank the aircraft out of the turn and onto the heading existing at the time of engagement.

3
Sensing of Attitude Changes

Under automatically controlled flight conditions, the sensing of all changes in aircraft attitude is accomplished by referencing them against some form of stabilised device comprising the primary element of inner loop stabilisation. The device universally adopted for this purpose, from the earliest types of control system to those now current, has been the gyroscope. In addition to the gyroscope it is also the practice in many cases to adopt a pendulous device which, although not purely stabilising in function, can serve as 'back up' to a gyroscope by sensing short-term attitude changes brought about by the effects of accelerations, vertical speed changes, and by sideslip.

The Gyroscope and its properties

A gyroscope is basically a mechanical device, the essential element of which is a heavy metal wheel, or rotor, spinning at high angular velocity about a spin axis. In order to provide spinning freedom, the rotor shaft is pivoted in a ring which is, in turn, pivoted in a second ring; the rings are known as the inner and outer gimbal rings respectively. The whole assembly comprises what is known as the gimbal system of a *free or space gyroscope* in that the spin axis, XX, remains fixed in space. The gimbal system is pivot-mounted in a frame as shown in fig. 3.1. The foregoing pivoting arrangements of the gimbal rings permit the gyroscope to have two degrees of freedom: (i) tilting freedom of the inner ring and rotor about the horizontal axis YY_1, and (ii) veering freedom of the complete gimbal system about the vertical axis ZZ_1.

In operation, the gyroscope possesses two important fundamental properties: gyroscopic inertia or rigidity, and precession. Both these properties depend on the principle of conservation of angular momen-

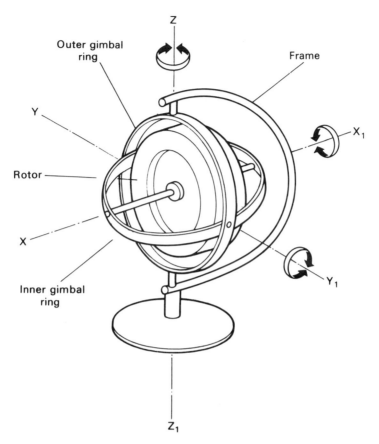

Fig. 3.1 Free gyroscope

tum, i.e. the angular momentum of a body about a given point remains constant unless some force is applied to change it; the properties form the subjects of the first and second laws of gyrodynamics respectively.

Rigidity

This property resists any force which tends to change the plane of rotation of the rotor of a gyroscope, and is dependent on three factors: (i) the mass of the rotor, (ii) the angular momentum of the rotor, and (iii) the distance at which the mass acts from the axis of rotation, i.e. the radius of gyration.

Precession

Precession is the angular rate of change in the direction of the plane of rotation under the influence of an applied force. The rate of change is proportional to the strength of the applied force, and inversely proportional to the moment of inertia of the rotor and the angular momentum of the rotor.

Fig. 3.2 a illustrates a free gyroscope, the rotor of which is assumed to be spinning, with constant angular momentum ω in an anti-clockwise direction. If a force F is applied upward at the inner ring then, as with any body which may be moved about some axis, the force will produce a torque T (equal to the product of the force and the distance at which it acts from the centre of the rotor) about the axis YY_1. Since a gyroscope possesses rigidity, any tendency for the torque to produce tilting of the inner ring and rotor about axis YY_1, is resisted. The complete gyroscope will, however, precess at a constant angular velocity about the axis ZZ_1, and in a direction at right-angles to the applied force.

A simple rule of thumb method of determining the direction in which a gyroscope will precess is to consider that the applied force acts at right-angles to the plane of spin, and at a point directly on the rotor rim (point 'A' in fig. 3.2 a). If the point is carried around the rotor and through 90° in the direction of rotation (point 'B') that will be the point at which the force and resulting torque are apparently acting.

The direction in which precession of a gyroscope takes place is dependent on the direction of rotation of its rotor, and on the direction of the applied force. This may be noted by comparing diagram b of fig. 3.2, with diagram a. As soon as the force and torque are withdrawn precession ceases, but if they are continually applied precession will continue until the plane of spin of the rotor is aligned with the plane of the applied force.

In connection with gyroscopic attitude sensing devices, it is usual to mutually associate the axes YY_1 and ZZ_1 with the spin axis and to relate them to input and output functions. Thus, the axis about which a torque is applied is termed the input axis and the one about which precession takes place is termed the output axis.

Limitations of a free gyroscope

The free or space gyroscope we have thus far considered would serve no useful purpose as an aircraft attitude sensing device, since an aircraft in flight is still very much an 'earth-bound' vehicle. Thus, all attitude references must be with respect to the earth. It is required therefore, that a free gyroscope be corrected in some way to take into account the effects of such factors as the earth's rotation and the transport of the gyroscope from one point on the earth to another.

Effects of the earth's rotation
Since the earth rotates about its axis 360° every day its rate of rotation is 15° per hour, and in association with gyrodynamics, this is termed the earth rate (ω_e). Depending on the orientation of the spin axis and input axis (as defined earlier) of a free or space gyroscope, it will sense various components of the earth rate as an angular input, and to an

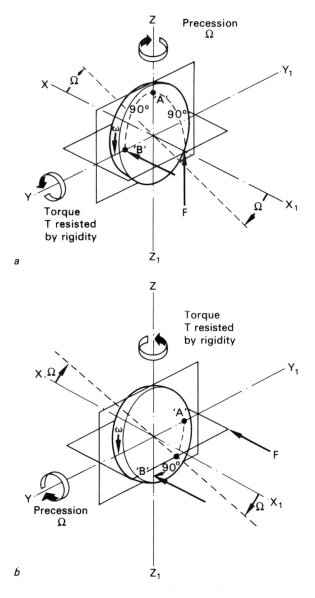

Fig. 3.2 Gyroscopic precession

observer on the earth the gyroscope would appear to veer, or drift as it is normally termed in this context.

Let us consider first a gyroscope positioned at a latitude λ ('A' in

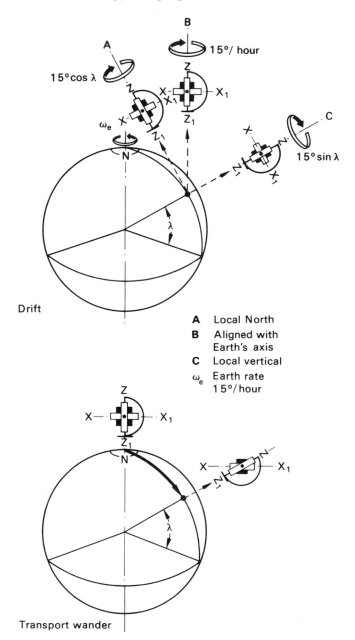

Fig. 3.3 Drift and transport wander

70

fig. 3.3) so that its spin axis is horizontal, and its input axis (ZZ_1 in this case) is aligned with the local N–S component of the earth's rate at this latitude. To an observer at the gyroscope's position, the gyroscope rotor and gimbal system would appear to drift in a horizontal plane relative to the frame; the drift rate would be equal to $15°\cos\lambda$. Drift would also be apparent at position 'B', but since in this case the input axis is aligned with the earth's axis, the drift rate would be equal to the earth's rate, i.e. 15° per hour. When the input axis is aligned with the local vertical component of the earth's rate (position 'C'), the apparent drift would be equal to $15°\sin\lambda$. If the input axis were aligned with the local E–W component of the earth's rate, there would be no apparent drift since rotor rotation and earth rotation are both in the same plane.

Effects of transporting a gyroscope over the earth's surface

Let us again consider the effects on a horizontal axis gyroscope which is set up initially at the North Pole, with its input axis aligned with that of the earth then, as we have already observed, it would exhibit earth rate drift. Assume now that the gyroscope is transported to a lower latitude and with its input axis aligned with the local vertical component of the earth's rate. During the time of transport, it will have appeared to an observer on the earth that the spin axis of the gyroscope has tilted in a vertical plane, until at the new latitude λ it appears to be in the position shown. Apparent tilt, or transport wander as it is called, would also be observed if, during transport, the input axis were aligned with either a local N–S component or a local E–W component of the earth's rate. Since the transported gyroscope is also rotating with the earth the tilt and earth rate drift are simultaneous effects which, during one complete rotation of the earth, would make the gyroscope appear to trace out a conical path. A free gyroscope having a vertical spin axis would, on the other hand, only exhibit apparent tilt.

The relationship between earth rate, transport wander and input axis alignment are summarised in the following table.

| | Input axis alignment | | |
	Local north	Local east	Local vertical
Earth rate	$\omega_e\cos\lambda$	nil	$\omega_e\sin\lambda$
Transport wander	$\dfrac{U}{R}$	$\dfrac{V}{R}$	$\dfrac{U}{R}\tan\lambda$

ω_e = earth's angular velocity
λ = latitude
R = earth's radius
V = north–south component of transport velocity
U = east–west component of transport velocity

Earth or 'tied' gyroscope

In order to utilise a free gyroscope as a practical attitude sensing element, compensations must be made which will minimise earth rate drift and transport wander to the fullest extent and, by so doing, will maintain the axis in the required mutual positions relative to the earth. Thus, the gyroscope must be converted into what is commonly termed an earth or 'tied' gyroscope.

Various compensation methods are adopted, and some examples will be described later in this chapter. At this juncture it may be noted, however, that the methods are, fundamentally, based on gravity sensing and the utilisation of the property of precession.

Gimbal lock and tumbling

Gimbal lock is a phenomenon which can occur when the rotor spin axis of a two-degrees-of-freedom gyroscope, coincides with the outer gimbal ring axis, i.e. the inner ring has turned through 90°. Under such conditions the gyroscope no longer has two-degrees of freedom and, if it is turned, a force will be applied to the inner gimbal ring to precess the outer gimbal ring into a continuous spin. Once spinning has begun the gimbal rings remain locked regardless of the attitude assumed by the gyroscope thereafter. To prevent gimbal lock, mechanical stops are incorporated, e.g. in a vertical axis gyroscope freedom about the pitch axis is normally restricted to $\pm85°$ of motion.

The use of stops presents another problem. When they contact the outer ring it precesses through 180° about its axis, such motion being known as 'tumbling'. However, it is very seldom that the instrument pitch limits are exceeded under normal operating conditions.

Nutation

A two-degrees-of-freedom gyroscope is also susceptible to a phenomenon known as nutation, which is simply a wobbling of the rotor spin axis. It is, in effect, a self-sustaining oscillation which physically represents a transfer of energy from one degree of freedom and back again. In contrast to precessional motion, nutation needs no external torque to sustain it. It is minimised by having as large a rotor angular momentum as possible in conjunction with gimbal rings having low moments of inertia.

Gimballing errors

These errors occur when the angular motions of gimbal rings do not correspond to the actual motion about their reference axes. For example, when a horizontal axis gyroscope (as used for directional references) is tilted on inter-cardinal headings and then turned, the azimuth indication will be in error.

Attitude references established by gyroscopes

Gyroscopes establish reference data against which changes in an aircraft's pitch, roll, and yaw (or direction) attitudes may be sensed and for this purpose two types of earth gyroscope are adopted: the displacement gyroscope and the rate gyroscope.

Displacement gyroscope

A displacement gyroscope is one which has two degrees of freedom, and can be used for detecting angular displacements about the fixed datum established by the property of rigidity. For the establishment of a directional reference, a gyroscope having its spin axis horizontal is employed (fig. 3.4 a). A displacement gyroscope is also used for establishing pitch and roll attitude references, but as will be noted from diagram b the gyroscope spin axis is, in this case, vertical. The operating details of some typical attitude sensing devices employing displacement gyroscopes are given on pages 74 to 77.

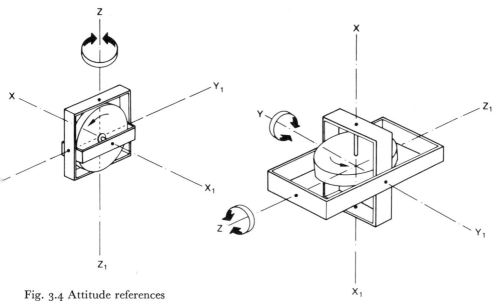

Fig. 3.4 Attitude references
a Directional reference about axis ZZ_1
b Pitch attitude reference about axis YY_1. Roll attitude reference about axis ZZ_1

Rate gyroscope

Unlike a displacement gyroscope, a rate gyroscope (fig. 3.4 *c*) is constrained to only one degree of freedom, and it detects the angular rate at which displacements about a selected input axis takes place. It utilises the property of precession for this purpose, the precession occurring in proportion to the rate at which displacements occur, equilibrium being established between precession and some form of controlled restraint (e.g. a spring). Some typical rate gyroscope attitude sensing devices are described on pages 78 to 90.

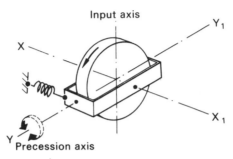

Fig. 3.4*c* Rate gyroscope

Displacement type sensing elements

The most common applications of horizontal-axis and vertical-axis displacement gyroscopes, relate to the standard flight instruments known as the directional gyro and the gyro horizon respectively. Since both these instruments are, in fact, adapted for use as directional, pitch, and roll attitude sensors in some automatic flight control systems (see fig. 2.5), they also serve as a useful introduction to the operating principles employed in the independent vertical reference sensing units associated with the more sophisticated flight control and flight director systems.

Directional gyro

This instrument provides a stabilised directional reference for maintaining a desired heading, and for turning on to a new heading. The outer gimbal ring of the gyroscope is pivoted about its vertical axis in the instrument case and has a circular card, graduated in degrees, secured to it. The card is referenced against a fixed lubber line, and is visible through a rectangular opening in the front of the instrument case. In some types of directional gyro (the one in fig. 2.5 for example), the graduated card is in the form of a flat disc and geared to the outer gimbal ring so that it rotates in a vertical plane. With the instrument in operation, gyroscopic rigidity stabilises the gyroscope and card, and a certain heading is referenced against the lubber line. If the aircraft heading changes, the instrument case and lubber line turn with the aircraft about the gyroscope thus giving an indication of the number of degrees through which the aircraft turns. Since a directional gyro is non-magnetic, and is also subject to a long-term wander, its heading indications must be set to correspond with those of the magnetic compass. This is achieved by a setting knob at the front of the instrument. When the knob is pushed in, it engages a locking, or caging, mechanism with the gyroscope gimbal system which can then be rotated to the desired heading by turning the setting knob.

From this outline of how stabilised heading indications are obtained, it will be apparent that by coupling an electrical pick-off element to the gimbal system of a directional gyro, directional sensing signals can also be obtained for the purpose of automatically maintaining desired headings, and turning an aircraft on to new headings. Details of how this is achieved will be given in chapter 6.

The rotors of directional gyroscopes are pneumatically operated either by connecting them to the vacuum side of an engine driven vacuum pump, or to the pressure side of such a pump. In each case air passes through a jet system in the gimbal rings and spins the rotor by impinging on 'buckets' cut in the periphery of the rotor.

Gyro horizon

The gyro horizon provides visual indications of any change of pitch and roll attitudes by the relative positions of two elements; one symbolising the aircraft itself, and the other in the form of a bar stabilised by a vertical gyroscope and symbolising the natural horizon. The spin axis of the gyroscope is maintained in the vertical position by a gravity sensing device (see page 92). Supplementary indications of roll are presented by the position of a pointer, also gyro stabilised, and a fixed roll angle scale. The gimbal system is arranged so that the inner gimbal ring forms the rotor casing and is pivoted parallel to the aircraft's lateral axis YY_1; and the outer gimbal ring is pivoted parallel to the aircraft's fore-and-aft axis ZZ_1. The outer gimbal ring pivots are located at the front and rear ends of the instrument case. The element symbolising the aircraft may be either rigidly fixed to the case or externally adjusted up and down for pitch trim setting.

In operation, the gimbal system is stabilised so that in level flight the three axes are mutually at right angles. When there is a change in the aircraft's attitude (it goes into a climb, say) the instrument case and outer gimbal ring will turn about the axis YY_1 of the stabilised inner gimbal ring. The horizon bar is pivoted at the side, and to the rear of the outer gimbal ring, and engages an actuating pin fixed to the inner gimbal ring, thus forming a magnifying lever system. In a climb attitude the bar pivot carries the rear end of the bar upwards causing it to pivot about the stabilised actuating pin. The front end of the bar and the pointer therefore move downwards through a greater angle than that of the outer gimbal ring and, since movement is relative to the symbolic aircraft element, a climbing attitude is indicated.

Changes in the lateral attitude of the aircraft, i.e. a roll to the left or right, turn the instrument case about the axis ZZ_1 and the whole stabilised gimbal system. Hence, lateral attitude changes are indicated by movement of the symbolic aircraft element relative to the horizon bar, and also by relative movement between the roll angle scale and the pointer. A background plate which symbolises the sky is fixed to the front end of the outer gimbal ring and carries a roll pointer which registers against the roll angle scale.

In applying this instrument to the automatic control of an aircraft suitable pick-off elements are mounted on the pitch and roll axes of the gimbal system (see chapter 4).

Gyro horizons may also be operated pneumatically, and in a manner similar to that adopted for directional gyros. However, in many applications the gyroscope is a 3-phase squirrel-cage induction motor which operates from a 115 volt, a.c. 400 Hz supply.

Electrically-operated gyroscopes

One of the essential requirements for any gyroscope is to have the mass of the rotor concentrated as near to the periphery as possible, thus ensuring maximum inertia. This presents no difficulty where solid metal rotors (as employed in air-driven instruments) are concerned, but when adapting electric motors as gyroscopes some rearrangement of their basic design is necessary in order to achieve the desired effect. An induction motor normally has its rotor revolving inside the stator, but to make one small enough for use as a gyroscopic sensing element, would result in too small a rotor mass and inertia. However, by designing the rotor and its bearings so that a section of it can also rotate on the outside of the stator, then for the same required size of motor the mass of the rotor is concentrated further from the centre, so that the radius of gyration, and the inertia, are increased. This is the method adopted not only in gyro horizons, but in all instruments and systems employing electrically-operated gyroscopes.

Vertical reference units

In more advanced types of flight control systems, displacements in pitch and roll are also referenced against a vertical-axis gyroscope, but instead of forming part of a panel-mounted instrument as hitherto described, the gyroscope is incorporated in a unit which is located at some remote point within the aircraft. Thus, the unit can serve as a central transmitting source of attitude information not only for a flight control system but also for attitude indicators which form part of a flight director system (see chapter 8). A typical vertical reference unit is shown in fig. 3.5.

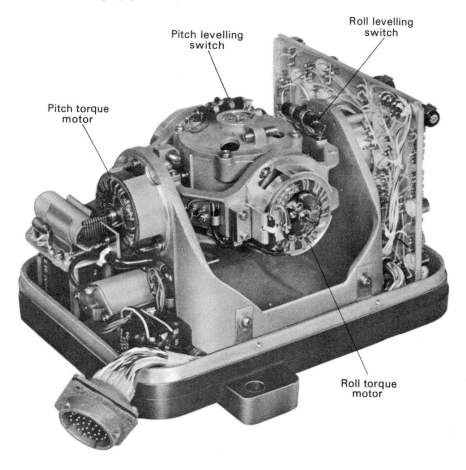

Fig. 3.5 Vertical reference unit

Rate type sensing elements

In several types of automatic flight control systems, the sensing of aircraft attitude changes is accomplished by rate gyroscopes which, as noted earlier are single-degree-of-freedom gyroscopes utilising the property of precession. The resultant movements of the rotor, and gimbal ring, position the moving element of an electrical signal pick-off element. Rotors are electrically driven, and the power supply required depends on the type of aircraft and the automatic flight control system applied to it. For example, in certain types of light aircraft employing a single-axis control system (see chapter 3), the power supply required is 28 volts direct current, while for larger aircraft employing more sophisticated systems, the gyroscopes operate from a 115 volt alternating current supply.

As an attitude change sensing device, a rate gyroscope has several advantages over a displacement gyroscope, the principal of which are (i) more rapid detection of small attitude changes since the time interval of the angular velocity is not involved, and (ii) smoother corrective action without 'overshoot' tendencies, because control signals are provided at a rate proportional to that at which attitude changes occur (called 'rate/rate control').

Rate gyroscope principle

It will be noted from fig. 3.6 that freedom of movement about the output or precession axis of a rate gyroscope is restrained, in this case, by a spring connected between the gimbal ring and casing. The spring, which may be of the linear or torsional type, has a characteristic which

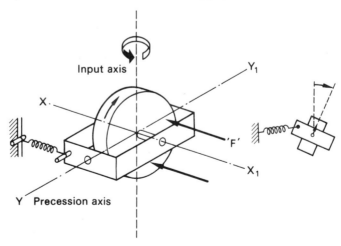

Fig. 3.6 Rate gyroscope principle

is calibrated to balance the precession produced at the appropriate rates of torque input. An alternative method of restraint adopted in some designs is one employing a force-balance, or force-feedback system, (see also page 84) whereby a torque is generated electrically to balance the precession, and by means of a torque motor the gimbal ring is restrained at a null position. The current flowing through the torque motor thus becomes a measure of the rate of torque input.

When a rate gyroscope is in its normal operating position the rotor spin axis will always be horizontal due to the spring restraint, and the moving element of the signal pick-off will be at the zero datum. With the rotor spinning, its rigidity will further ensure that the zero datum is maintained. When, however, the gyroscope is turned about a vertical input axis, the rigidity of the gyroscope resists the turning, but it tilts in one direction or the other about the precession axis YY_1 depending on the direction of turn; the effects of a turn to the left are indicated in fig. 3.6. Precession continues until it is balanced by the restraining force created by the stretching of the spring. Since the precession of a rate gyroscope is equal to the product of angular momentum of the rotor, and the rate of turn, the spring force is then a measure of the rate of turn.

In practical applications, the gimbal ring deflection is generally limited by stops to not more than 2°, the reason for this being to reduce the cross-coupling error due to the rate-of-turn component not being at right angles to the spin axis during gimbal ring deflection.

It should be noted that a rate gyroscope requires no erecting device or correction for random drift, for the simple reason that it is always centred at its zero datum position by the appropriate system of spring restraint. Since precession plays such an important part in the operation of rate gyroscopes, it is essential for the rotor speed to be maintained constant. This is ensured by providing direct current powered gyroscopes with a centrifugal governing device, while in the case of gyroscopes powered by alternating current the supply frequency is maintained constant.

Typical rate sensors

An example of an alternating current-operated rate sensor is shown in fig. 3.7, and although of an early design it is typical of the majority of sensors currently in use, in that the gyroscope is formed by a hysteresis motor. As usual when adopting an electric motor as a gyroscope, the rotating element is designed so that the greatest possible radius of gyration and moment of inertia, compatible with the speed and rate measurements required, and the overall physical dimensions of the gyroscope, are obtained.

GYRO CASING

"I" BAR OF PICK-OFF

"E" CORE OF PICK-OFF

FRICTIONLESS ELECTRICAL CONNECTIONS TO GYRO

DATUM ADJUSTMENT OF PICK-OFF

LEAF-SPRING SUSPENSION

3 PHASE GYRO TERMINALS

PICK-OFF TERMINALS

PICK-OFF MOUNTING

Fig. 3.7 Rate sensor

The motor consists of a hard steel rotor fitting closely over a laminated three-phase, star-wound twelve-pole stator supplied with 115 volts a.c. at a constant frequency of 400 Hz. The power supply sets up a rotating magnetic field within the stator which, in turn, induces magnetism of opposite polarities in the cobalt steel ring forming part of the rotor. As a result of the hysteresis characteristics of the driving ring, the rotor is made to revolve with the rotating field of the stator until finally both are in synchronism at a running speed of 12 000 rev/min. The principle is illustrated in fig. 3.8.

The rotor undergoes magnetisation and demagnetisation as the strength of the stator field changes; if the flux density B is plotted against the magnetising force H the result is the familiar hysteresis loop from which the motor derives its name (fig. 3.8 a). The area within the loop can be shown to be numerically equal to the energy consumed in the magnetisation/demagnetisation cycle, and it is this energy that drives the rotor.

Let us assume that at one particular instant the stator current induces magnetism of north polarity in stator pole 'A' (diagram b), magnetism will also be induced in the rotor, and a point 'x' immediately opposite pole 'A' will be of south polarity. During the next half-cycle of the magnetising current, the polarity of pole piece 'A' will change from north to south, and the adjacent pole piece 'B' will take on a north seeking polarity. The polarity at point 'x' on the rotor will at this stage be diminishing because of the polarity change taking place in pole piece 'A'. However, due to hysteresis effect, point 'x' will still be of south polarity while polarity changes are taking place in both pole

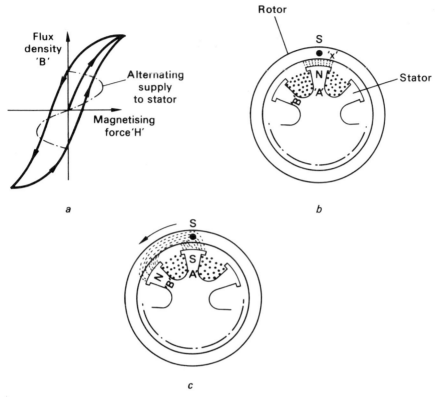

Fig. 3.8 Principle of hysteresis motor

pieces 'A' and 'B'. It will be seen therefore, (diagram c) that pole piece 'B' will now attract point 'x' causing the rotor to move in the same direction as the stator field.

The complete motor assembly is totally enclosed by a ventilated casing which forms the gimbal ring. The casing is mounted on pillars on the unit base plate by means of two leaf springs which not only provide the necessary restraint but also function as gimbal ring pivots. The electrical signal pick-off element is of the inductive variable magnetic coupling type, and consists of an I bar, which is positioned by the gyroscope, and a fixed E bar. The operation of this form of pick-off is described on page 103.

The emphasis on miniaturisation of airborne electronic equipment, and associated electro-mechanical components, has also significantly affected the design of rate gyroscopes, to the extent that miniature, sub-miniature and micro-miniature units are available to meet the attitude sensing requirements for specific types of aircraft. An example of a miniature unit is shown in fig. 3.9. The gyroscope is also formed by a three-phase hysteresis motor operating at a speed of 24 000 rev/min

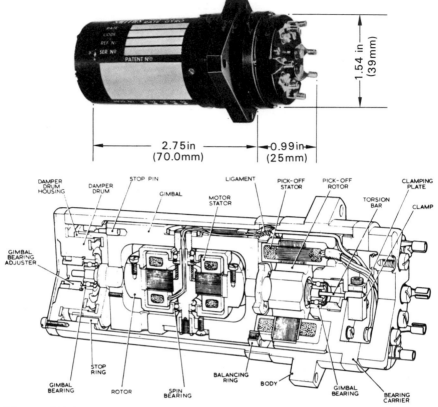

Fig. 3.9 Miniature rate gyroscope

from a 26 volt, 400 Hz a.c. supply. The rotor in this example is supported in precision type ball bearings but in some units the rotor runs in bearings formed by an inert gas, while in others the bearings are of the self-generating aerodynamic type. The gimbal ring is supported in ball bearings and is restrained by means of a torsion bar spring, the stiffness of which provides for a maximum rate of 60°/second. An electrical signal pick-off element is incorporated in the unit, and is also of the inductive variable magnetic coupling type; however, unlike the one used with the gyroscope shown in fig. 3.7, it consists of a rotor and a fixed stator.

An interesting example of a direct current operated rate gyroscope is that adopted in one of the 'Century' series of control systems developed by Edo-Aire Mitchell (see also page 89). The gyroscope serves as both a roll and yaw sensing element, and is unique in that the motor employs a photo-electric means of commutation as opposed to conventional brushes and commutator. The gyroscope rotor is magnetically polarised and housed within a coil assembly. One half of the rotor's peripheral surface is of reflective brass, while the other half is chemically etched to be non-reflective. When the power is off, this half of the rotor is exposed to an incandescent light source, and a photo-transistor, both of which are directed towards the rotor. When power is applied to the rotor coil, the current flow through it turns the rotor, and when the reflective half of its surface is exposed to the light source, the current flow is isolated. Momentum of the rotor, however, carries it round until the non-reflective half is again exposed. At this point, the cycle will repeat and the rotor continues to rotate. As the rotor gains speed, a feedback voltage is developed across the rotor coil, and after mixing with a reference voltage, it is applied to two switching transistors the functions of which are to regulate the rotor speed by switching the current on and off at a rate proportional to rotor rotation.

Damping of rate gyroscopes

In the design of rate gyroscopes it is also necessary to incorporate a system of damping restraint. Such a system should be as small as possible to ensure that the gyroscope will instantly respond to rate-of-turn changes, and at the same time, provide sufficient restraint to damp out any oscillations. The damping methods adopted vary between manufacturers, but in general, they fall into three principal classes (i) eddy current, (ii) fluid, and (iii) air dashpot.

The eddy current damping system, which is adopted for the rate gyroscope shown in fig. 3.7, consists of a counterpoised toothed quadrant, actuated by deflections of the gyroscope and in mesh with a pinion. On the same shaft as the pinion is a copper disc positioned between the faces of a two-pole permanent magnet. When the gyroscope is deflected to one or other side of its zero datum position, the quadrant is also deflected to rotate the disc past the magnet pole faces. Eddy currents are thereby induced in the disc, the resultant effect of which is to oppose the motion of the disc and so provide a damped or 'dead beat' movement of the gyroscope. The effects of inertia on the copper disc are reduced by friction loading between it and its shaft, and for a similar reason, movement of the quadrant is controlled by a pair of pre-adjusted springs.

Fluid damping systems are used in certain types of miniature and sub-miniature rate gyroscopes, e.g. the one illustrated in fig. 3.9, and in operation, are dependent on the viscous shear of a silicone fluid contained in the space between a damper drum and its housing. Deflections of the gyroscope produce relative motion between the drum and housing, but owing to its viscosity the oil produces a force to oppose the motion. Although silicone fluid has a relatively low variation of viscosity with temperature, it is usually necessary to compensate for

83

changes to ensure that the damping ratio is kept within acceptable limits over the operating temperature range of the gyroscope.

The air dashpot method of damping is based on that which has been in use for many years in turn-and-bank indicators. Pistons are linked to the gimbal ring, and whenever it is deflected they move in and out of their respective cylinders fixed to the gyroscope frame or casing. As the pistons move, air passes through small bleed holes in the cylinders, the size of which can be pre-adjusted to provide the required degree of damping.

Force-balance rate gyroscope

A force-balance, or force feedback, rate gyroscope operates on the same fundamental principle as its conventional counterpart, but instead of utilising spring balancing force as a measure of the rate of turn or torque input, balancing is achieved electrically by a torque motor acting on the gimbal ring. The torque motor is connected to the pick-off sensing element via a high-gain amplifier; thus, when the gyroscope is turned about its input axis, precession of the gimbal ring is detected by the pick-off element, and a signal is transmitted to the amplifier. The amplifier signal is then transmitted to the torque motor in which an electromagnetic field is generated to produce a torque equal and opposite to the input torque so that the gimbal ring is restrained at its null position. In other words, the pick-off element serves only as a null detector, and the torque motor system functions as a stiff electrical spring. Since the torque is precisely related to the current flowing through the torque motor, the current may be used directly as a rate signal output to the appropriate control channel. Damping is achieved by incorporating suitable shaping networks in the feedback amplifier, thereby eliminating the need for any of the methods adopted for conventional spring-restrained gyroscopes.

In some types of force-balance gyroscope, the pick-off element is of the optical type consisting of a light emitting diode, two photo-electric cells, and a vane attached to the gimbal ring. The diode generates infra-red radiation which is sensed by the two cells. The vane is positioned between the diode and the cells and it differentially obscures the radiation when the gimbal ring is displaced. The outputs from the photo-electric cells are combined and amplified and then supplied to a moving-coil type of torque motor which drives the gyroscope and pick-off element to the balance position.

Rate sensing about three axes

From the description given earlier of the operating principle of the rate gyroscope, we have observed that sensing of a turn is a direct result of precession caused by movement about a vertical input axis or, what is the same thing, movement of the gyroscope in the yawing plane. It should, therefore, be apparent that if two additional rate gyroscopes can be positioned in an aircraft such that one can respond to movement in the pitching plane, and the other to movement in the rolling plane, then the resulting precession and spring balancing force in each case will be a measure of 'turn rates' in these two planes. We thus have the basis of a combined system for sensing the rates at which attitude changes occur in relation to all three axes of an aircraft, the disposition of the gyroscopes being arranged as shown in fig. 3.10.

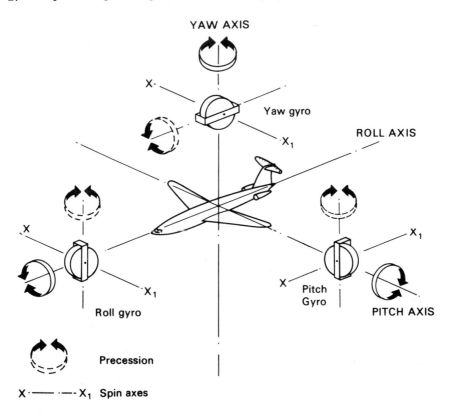

Fig. 3.10 Attitude sensing by rate gyroscopes

Fig. 3.11 illustrates a combined system utilising rate gyroscopes of the type shown in fig. 3.7. The gyroscopes are mounted on a platform which is supported in a gimbal assembly made up of a roll frame and an outer ring. The platform is pivoted within the roll frame and this, in turn, is pivoted within the outer ring; relative movement between

Fig. 3.11 Unit employing three rate gyroscopes

the three units and the aircraft being obtained only when manually-controlled manoeuvres are to be carried out through the medium of the automatic flight control system. However, to allow for the detection of disturbances from level flight attitudes resulting, say from atmospheric turbulence, relative movements are not required, and the complete gimbal system may therefore be regarded as a stable platform fixed to the aircraft.

The gyro platform is geared to an electric motor which can rotate the platform in pitch relative to the aircraft, while the roll frame is geared to a second motor so that both the frame and the platform can be related in roll relative to the aircraft. The motors are independently controlled by pitch and turn controls on a pilot's control unit. For example, if the pilot requires to manoeuvre the aircraft into a climb, he would operate the pitch control, which would then energise the platform motor causing it to tilt the platform forward. The pitch rate gyroscope detects this movement as an apparent nose-down displacement of the aircraft, and an appropriate signal is induced in its pick-off element. The signal is then transmitted to the pitch control channel for amplification and phase sensing, and finally to a servomotor coupled to the elevators causing them to be moved upwards. The aircraft thus adopts a nose-up attitude, the change in pitch occurring at the same angular rate as that at which the gyroscope platform is being tilted, and as these changes are in opposing directions the platform is maintained level in space. At the same time, and because the complete gimbal assembly can move with the aircraft, the pitch rate gyroscope will also detect the nose-up attitude, so that its pick-off element will transmit an opposing signal to the pitch control channel and servomotor, which causes the latter to move the elevators progressively back to their neutral or streamline position. When the desired climb angle is attained, the pitch control on the pilot's control unit is released and no further signals are transmitted.

In a similar manner, the turn control on the pilot's control unit initiates turning of the aircraft. In this case, both the roll frame and platform are rotated in roll relative to the aircraft by the roll platform motor. The rotation is detected by the roll rate gyroscope, and the signal from its pick-off element is transmitted to the roll servomotor which displaces the ailerons causing the aircraft to roll into a turn. Since the complete gimbal system turns with the aircraft, the yaw rate gyroscope detects the rate of turn as an apparent yaw displacement and it therefore attempts to reduce the roll angle and so oppose the turn set up by the roll rate gyroscope. This is prevented, however, by a 'turn demand' potentiometer device which is so arranged that a signal related to roll angle, rate of turn, and airspeed is produced in the aileron and rudder channels, to provide coordination of the turn. The turn is maintained until the turn control knob is restored to its normal central position, and at which the roll platform motor runs in the reverse direction to rotate the roll frame and platform to a level position in space. At the same time, the roll rate gyroscope detects this as an apparent roll displacement in the opposite direction, and an appropriate signal is transmitted to the roll servomotor which moves the ailerons back to their neutral position thereby returning the aircraft to a level flight attitude on its new heading.

For the detection of disturbances of the aircraft from a level flight attitude, the complete gimbal assembly may be regarded as a stable platform fixed to the aircraft. Thus when the aircraft is disturbed there will be no relative movement between it and the platform, and the relevant rate gyroscope and servomotor control channels will maintain the aircraft and platform level.

Fig. 3.12 illustrates another example of the method of rate sensing about three axes. In this case, the unit which is referred to as a three-axis rate transmitter, is used in conjunction with a vertical gyroscope unit (see page 90). Unlike the unit described in the preceding para-

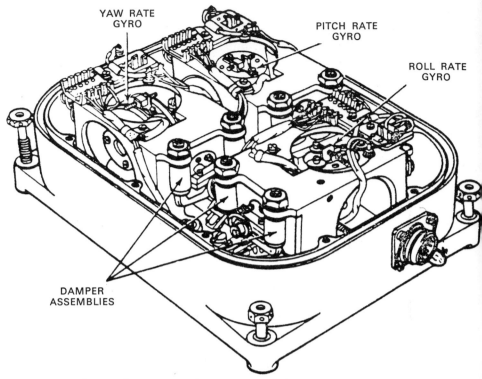

YAW RATE
GYRO

PITCH RATE
GYRO

ROLL RATE
GYRO

DAMPER
ASSEMBLIES

Fig. 3.12 Three-axis rate transmitter

graphs, the rate gyroscopes are mounted on a fixed base, and are enclosed in an hermetically-sealed case. Other differences relate to the manner in which the gyroscopic axes are disposed, and in the method of error sensing; in this case, the pick-off elements are synchro transmitters. The gyroscopes are spring-restrained, and are damped by individual dashpot assemblies.

Single-axis rate sensing

For certain types of light aircraft, automatic control systems are available for the purpose of providing simple wing-levelling or roll control, and yaw damping, via the ailerons only. In such systems, sensing is by means of a single rate gyroscope.

As noted earlier, the sensing attitude changes about the roll and yaw axes of an aircraft can be effected by the relative positioning of the input and output axes of two rate gyroscopes. However, since the spin axes of both gyroscopes are in the same horizontal direction (see fig. 3.10), then if we take either one of the gyroscopes and mount it so that its gimbal ring and precession axis are tilted at an angle (30° is a typical value) from the horizontal, it alone will sense both roll and yaw attitude changes. Examples of this sensing method are to be found in instruments known as turn co-ordinators, and as turn and bank stabiliser/trackers, the latter forming an optional feature in certain of the Edo-Aire Mitchell 'Century' series of control system for the provision of turn rate commands, and VOR radial and ILS localiser beam tracking.

Self monitored rate gyroscopes

The operation of any automatic flight control system is, of course, dependent on a high standard of operating integrity of each of the elements constituting the system. For systems designed to provide the fullest automatic control capability, i.e. from control engagement through approach and landing phases (see chapter 9), it follows that the standard must be of the highest, and furthermore it must be extended to embrace methods of rapidly detecting any failure that might occur in any one of the individual elements. In the development of such systems, therefore, design studies resulted in the application of techniques whereby certain elements could be self-monitoring and so themselves provide indications of their failure to operate. The overall application of this failure-monitoring technique is referred to as in-line monitoring, and one of the elements associated with the technique is a type of rate gyroscope which operates on the force-balance principle (see page 84).

The faults most likely to occur are those affecting the operation of the force feedback loop, and the loss of angular momentum of the gyroscope. The feedback loop could become ineffective as a result of, say, loss of power supplies, faults in the pick-off torque motor and in the force feedback amplifier. The fact that the gyroscope's gimbal ring is always near its null region when the force feedback loop is operating correctly provides a means of monitoring this loop. If, for example, a coil of the torque motor becomes short-circuited, or even open-circuited, the gimbal ring will be rapidly deflected from its null position whenever a small movement about the gyroscope's input axis takes place. A monitoring system which can, therefore, produce an output and detect changes in the output whenever the gimbal ring is not in its null position can also indicate a fault. Angular momentum is, among other things, dependent on the speed of rotor rotation, and so any changes in an output/speed relationship can also be indicated by a monitoring system as a fault. Thus, the basic function of in-line monitoring when applied to a rate gyroscope of the force-balance type is to monitor gimbal ring null angle, and rotor speed.

Monitoring is carried out by a single monitor pick-off, consisting of a small permanent magnet embedded in the rim of the gyroscope rotor, which induces a voltage in a pick-off coil fixed to the rotor casing so that a pulse is induced in the coil every revolution of the rotor (see diagram a, fig. 3.13). The magnetic circuit is designed so that the amplitude of the positive-going pulse is much larger than that of the negative pulse so that rotational sense of the rotor can be checked. In addition, the design of the magnetic circuit is such that the pick-off output falls off sharply when the gimbal ring is deflected away from its null position. The monitoring circuit then checks the amplitude (gimbal ring deflection) and frequency (rotor speed) of the pick-off pulse.

The monitor system is shown in b of fig. 3.13. The amplitude of the pulses is examined in the pulse level detection stage, which only produces an output when pulse amplitudes are within 70% of the maximum value. The pulse then discharges an integrating circuit, the d.c. level of which controls a bi-stable circuit, and, in turn, a relay or a solid-state switching circuit. Loss of pulses, as a result of either a failure causing the gimbal ring to remain uncaptured, or a decrease in pulse repetition frequency as a result of the rotor slowing down, causes the integrating circuit to charge up to a d.c. level sufficient to trigger the bi-stable circuit and so operate the relay, or switching circuit, and the associated warning annunciator.

Monitoring of jamming or seizure of the gimbal ring in its null position may also form part of the failure-monitoring technique. A square wave signal is injected into the input of the d.c. amplifier driving the torque motor. When the force feedback loop is operating correctly, the gimbal ring will deflect so that the pick-off signal 'backs off' the square-wave demand (see diagram c fig. 3.13). The resulting output in terms of the voltage across the torque motor will be a small 'blip' at the beginning and end of the square-wave as a result of the torque required to accelerate the gimbal ring. However, if the gimbal ring has seized up, the full square-wave input will appear across the torque motor coils. The monitor circuit 'gates' the output so that the start of the square-wave is ignored, and the d.c. level after phase-sensitive rectification is examined during the gating period.

Combined use of displacement and rate gyroscopes

A number of automatic flight control systems currently in service make use of error information, based not only on the magnitude of displacements of an aircraft and its flight control surfaces but also on the rate of change of these displacements. In these systems, a vertical axis gyroscope

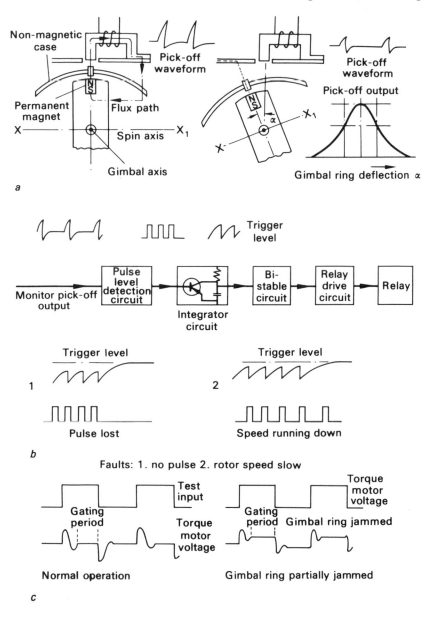

Fig. 3.13 Self-monitored rate gyroscope

unit detects displacements as a primary attitude change sensor, and applies appropriate corrective control, but as there is always a tendency for a displacement sensing device to cause 'overshoot' the displacement corrections are damped by rate signals from rate gyroscopes. When the displacement error is no longer changing, the rate signals fall to zero and the error existing at that instant is acted upon by control forces that are proportional only to the magnitude of the error.

Thus, by combining the signals from the attitude sensing elements coupled to each type of gyroscope, the possibility of large deviations from reference conditions is greatly reduced and smoother control application and stability of operation is obtained. Furthermore, very small displacement errors and signals which would otherwise not cause corrective action, if left to a vertical gyroscope alone, are detected more quickly by rate gyroscopes and can be built up into stronger corrective signals.

Compensation systems

As we learned earlier in this chapter, a free gyroscope must be 'tied' to the earth by gravity sensing, before it can be utilised as a practical aircraft attitude sensing element; this applies in particular to horizontal axis and vertical axis gyroscopes. It is necessary, therefore, to provide compensation systems which will erect gyroscopes to, and thereafter maintain them at, their appropriate reference datums.

The design of compensation (or erection) systems varies, but the majority are of the gravity-sensing type and in general fall into two main categories: mechanical and electrical. The construction and operation of some representative systems in current use are described on this and the following pages.

Mechanical systems

In a directional gyro the error due to earth-rate is compensated by deliberately unbalancing the inner gimbal ring so that a constant torque and precession are applied to the gimbal system. The unbalance is effected by fastening a small weight to the inner gimbal ring, and then adjusting it during initial calibration, to apply sufficient torque and precession of the outer gimbal ring, to cancel out the error of the latitude in which the instrument was calibrated. This adjustment is usually effective up to 60° of latitude change; beyond this figure a re-adjustment of the balancing nut is necessary.

Compensation of tendencies for the gyroscope spin-axis to wander from its horizontal position is usually achieved via the air-jet system, a typical arrangement being as shown in fig. 3.14. The air for spinning the rotor is passed through two jets (fixed to the outer ring) and in the horizontal position of the rotor the forces from each jet are the same. If the rotor wanders from the horizontal position, the relative positions

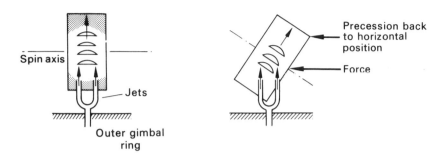

Fig. 3.14 Air-jet compensation system

between the jets and rotor are changed, such that the jet forces are unbalanced to produce a side force from one of the jets, the force causing the rotor to precess back to the horizontal position.

An early example of a mechanical system is the pendulous vane unit shown in fig. 3.15. The unit is applied to the air-driven gyro horizons of some types of basic flight control systems designed for use in light aircraft. It is fastened to the underside of the rotor housing and consists of four knife-edged pendulously suspended vanes clamped in pairs on two shafts; one parallel to the fore and aft axis of the aircraft and the other parallel to the athwartships axis. In the sides of the body there are four small elongated ports, one under each vane. The air, after having spun the gyroscope rotor, is exhausted through the ports, emerging as four streams; one forward, one rearward and two athwartships. When the gyroscope is in its normal vertical position the vanes hang vertically under the influence of gravity and each port is open by an equal amount. Thus, the reaction from each air stream is equal and the forces about each axis are in balance.

When the gyroscope is displaced from the vertical position about either the pitch or roll axis the appropriate pair of vanes remains vertical thereby causing the opening of one port to increase and the opening of the opposite port to decrease. The increased reaction of the air flowing from the greater opening results in a torque which, in effect, is applied at one point on the underside of the rotor. As the gyroscope rotor always moves at a point 90° away from the point of applied torque and in the direction of rotation, the rotor will precess back to the vertical until the port openings and air reactions are again equal.

A mechanical system which is adopted in some vertical reference units, is shown schematically in fig. 3.16. It is comprised of a circular magnet which is attached to and revolves at the same speed as the gyroscope rotor, a concentrically mounted drag cup, and two metal balls which run freely in a track attached to the inner gimbal ring. The field of the rotating magnet induces eddy currents in the drag cup and

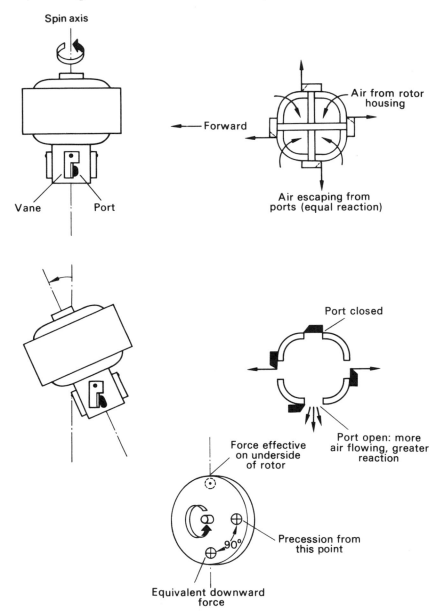

Fig. 3.15 Pendulous vane unit

the reaction from these currents causes it to rotate in the same direction as the magnet but at a speed of approximately 35 rev/min controlled by a governing device.

When the gyroscope is in its vertical position the ball track is

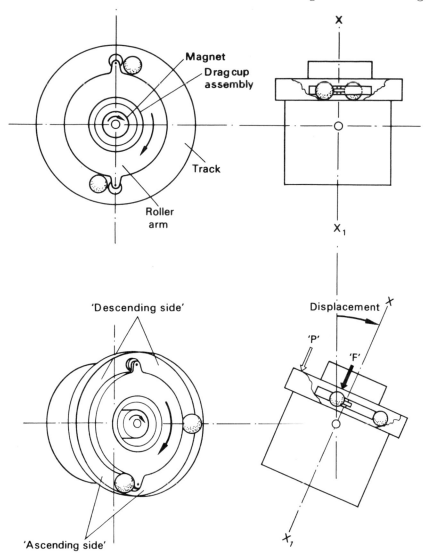

Fig. 3.16 Ball type erection system

horizontal, and the balls are propelled around the track by a roller arm at a constant speed. Since they are disposed 180° to each other, their weight is evenly distributed, and so a constant torque at a constant frequency is applied about each axis. As the average applied torque is zero no precession takes place.

Any wander of the gyroscope rotor will, however, cause the balls to move away from the roller arm to seek the lowest point on the track. Their speed will therefore no longer be constant because they now

95

descend the inclined track much faster than they can ascend. Furthermore, in spending a longer time on the ascent, the weight distribution of the balls becomes uneven, and is concentrated on what may be termed the 'ascending side' of the rotor. Thus, an average torque is applied at the appropriate equivalent point on the rotor causing it to precess, and thereby counteract the wander, and so restore the gyroscope to its vertical position.

Electrical systems

Compensation of earth-rate error by electrical means is normally applied to directional gyro units employed in remote-indicating compasses which provide directional command signals to automatic flight control systems. In one example the system consists of two small d.c. electromagnets built into the outer gimbal ring, one on either side of the inner gimbal ring bearing. One magnet is used in the northern hemisphere, and the other in the southern hemisphere, the d.c. supply for the magnet coils being selected via a latitude selector switch. Whenever the gyroscope rotor wanders through the magnetic field of an energised coil, eddy currents are induced in the rotor and, as a result, a torque is exerted on the inner gimbal ring which precesses the gimbal system in a direction opposite to that of the wander.

In applying an electrical method of compensating for wander of a directional gyro from its horizontal position, it is usual to adopt the one in which torques are applied by a torque motor controlled by a liquid-level switch. The electrical interconnection of these components is shown in fig. 3.17. The levelling switch is usually in the form of a sealed glass tube containing three electrodes which are immersed in an electrolytic fluid partially filling the tube. The tube is secured to the rotor housing parallel to the spin axis. The torque motor comprises a squirrel-cage type laminated-iron rotor mounted concentrically about a stator, the iron core of which has two windings: one providing a constant field and called the reference winding; and the other which is in two parts wound in opposition and called the control winding. The rotor is fixed to the directional gyro unit casing while the stator is free to rotate since it is fixed to the outer gimbal ring.

The system operates from one phase of a 115 volt alternating current supply, and as will be noted from fig. 3.17, power is applied directly to the centre electrode of the levelling switch and to the torque motor reference winding via capacitors. The function of the capacitors is to shift the phase of the current so as to lead the voltage by 90°, and thereby establish rotating magnetic fields within the stator core of the torque motor.

When the gyroscope is running and in its normal operating position

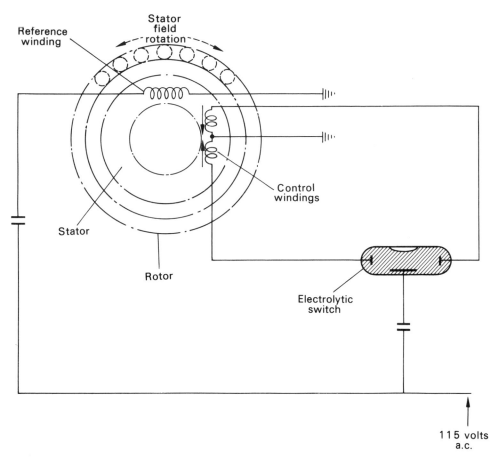

Fig. 3.17 Liquid-level switch and torque motor system

the outer electrodes of the levelling switch are immersed in equal amounts of fluid, so the circuit resistance of both parts of the torque motor control winding are in balance. The current flows are also in balance, and since the magnetic fields are in opposition they cancel each other and no net field is produced in the stator core. Let us now consider what happens when the gyroscope wanders from its normally horizontal position. The levelling switch will tilt so that one of its electrodes becomes only partially covered by the electrolytic fluid,

97

thereby decreasing the resistance in its part of the control winding circuit. Thus, the current flow and the magnetic field are no longer in balance and a resultant field is produced which rotates in the stator core in either a clockwise or anti-clockwise direction, depending on the direction of tilt of the levelling switch. As the field rotates, it cuts the closed circuit, bar-type conductors of the squirrel-cage rotor, causing a current to be induced in them. The effect of the induced current is to produce magnetic fields around the bars which interact with the rotating field causing a tendency for the rotor to follow this field. This tendency is, however, opposed because the rotor is fixed; consequently a reactive torque is set up in the torque motor, the torque causing the gyroscope rotor to precess back to the horizontal position, and thereby restore the levelling switch and control winding circuits to their balanced conditions.

The foregoing levelling switch and torque motor method of compensation in also applied to gyro horizons and vertical gyroscope units, but in such applications it is necessary to use two systems disposed as shown in fig. 3.18. The laterally-mounted switch detects wander of the gyroscope in roll, and is connected to its torque motor so that a corrective torque is applied relative to the pitch axis. Wander of the gyro in pitch is detected by the fore and aft mounted levelling switch which is connected to its torque motor so that corrective torques are relative to the roll axis. The manner in which torques and precession are produced by each system is the same as that already described. In some vertical gyroscope units the signals are supplied to the torque motors via signal amplifiers.

Errors in compensation systems

Since the vane type, and levelling switch type of compensation systems are of a pendulous nature they will be subjected to the forces which arise during turning, and acceleration or deceleration of the aircraft, and as a result a gyroscope can be precessed to a false position. As an example of how this occurs we may consider the effects on a levelling switch and torque motor system as used for vertical axis gyroscopes.

The forces acting on a switch displace the electrolytic fluid to one or other end of the tube thereby unbalancing the resistance of the torque motor control winding circuits, e.g. when the aircraft accelerates, the fluid in the pitch levelling switch is displaced to the rear of its tube, in the same way as if the top of the gyroscope axis had tilted to the rear. Thus, the pitch torque motor will cause the gyroscope to precess so that its axis is tilted forward from its true vertical position until the fluid in the levelling switch restores a balanced condition in the control winding circuit and precession ceases. The gyroscope is left in this false vertical position so that a false climbing attitude indication, and/or climb

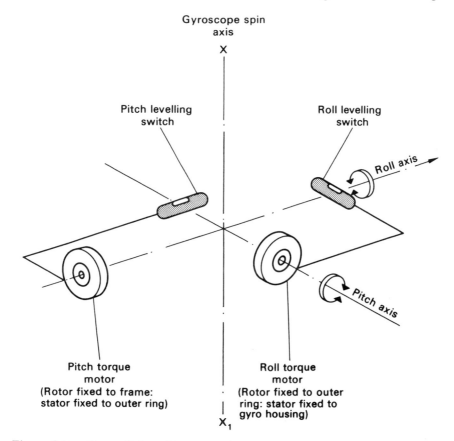

Fig. 3.18 Levelling switch and torque motor arrangement

command signal, would be produced until the cessation of the accelerating force. Conversely, a false descending attitude indication and/or
descend command signal would be produced under the influence of a
decelerating force.

During turns, the electrolytic fluid in the roll levelling switch is
displaced by centrifugal force, and so in a similar manner, the roll
torque motor will precess the gyroscope to a dynamic vertical to
produce a false left or right roll indication or command signal. This
rather complicates matters because, with the gyroscope spin axis tilted
into the centre of a turn, the axis traces out a conical path so that the
tilt also has a component about the pitch axis; in other words, a
'gimballing effect' is created. Thus, the force due to turning can also
cause false pitch attitude indications or command signals.

There are three principal methods of correcting the foregoing errors,
each of which can vary in application depending on the particular
design of gyro horizon or vertical gyro unit as the case may be. The

simplest method, and one which is adopted in some gyro horizons, is to impart a constant forward or rearward tilt to the spin axis by deliberately unbalancing the gyroscope so that precession will overcome, within its prescribed limitations, the pitch error resulting from accelerating, decelerating or turning forces.

In connection with levelling switch and torque motor systems, however, error correction methods are of an electrical nature designed either (i) to disconnect the switch causing the error (pitch and roll cut-out) or (ii) to change over the functions of switches during turns (pitch/bank erection). In some applications both these methods are combined. The circuits are designed to operate at specific levels of acceleration and deceleration, and rates of turn, and to automatically reset and reinstate control of the gyroscope once the forces acting on the switches fall below these levels. A pitch/bank erection system corrects for both pitch and roll errors occurring during a turn, and in a typical application it does this by disconnecting the roll levelling switch, and transferring its function of controlling the roll torque motor to the pitch levelling switch. The method of disconnect and transfer varies; in some cases it is effected through additional levelling switches which serve as circuit cut-outs, while, in one particular design of vertical gyroscope unit, cut-out is effected by a specific value of yaw rate signal from a yaw rate gyroscope sensor.

Location of attitude sensing elements

The locations of attitude sensing elements, and in particular those which are remote from the flight crew compartment of an aircraft, have to be carefully chosen otherwise the inherent flexibility of the aircraft structure will be interpreted by sensing elements as attitude changes, and thereby result in a condition of unstable coupling between the aircraft and its automatic flight control system. Locations must, therefore, be in areas where flexural frequency sensing is at a minimum.

Acceleration and sideslip sensors

The gyroscopic elements so far described may be considered as sensors of the primary attitude changes. In matching an automatic flight control system to the aerodynamic characteristics of specific types of aircraft, however, it is also often necessary to meet the requirements for the sensing and damping of secondary short-period attitude changes such as accelerations, vertical speed changes, and also for the sensing and monitoring of sideslip. In such cases, therefore, it is usual to provide additional sensing elements which are more rapid in their response than displacement type and/or rate type sensors would be, and which can also serve as a 'back-up' to such sensors. Two types of sensors which are commonly used are (i) linear acceleromometers and (ii) pendulum monitors. Since in both cases, output signals are established from inductive type pick-off elements, their operating principles will be described in chapter 4.

4
Command Signal Detection

The attitude sensing elements employed in automatic flight control systems form the most vital part of the servomechanism loop since they detect attitude changes in terms of errors which demand monitoring and correction. Both these functions, however, cannot be performed by the elements alone, and in this respect they are not unlike the primary flight instruments in that they demand some action on the part of the pilot in his role as the error monitoring and correcting element in the control loop. In other words, it is necessary to provide error signal sensors which by suitable coupling to the attitude sensors will automatically detect the phase and magnitude of the errors, and transmit this intelligence to the output section of the servomechanism. Signal sensors, or 'pick-off' elements as they are often called, are normally of the inductive type, although in some basic types of autopilot the principle of variable capacitance is adopted: typical examples are considered in this chapter.

Inductive elements

The fundamental operating principle of inductive elements is based on that of the conventional transformer, i.e. for a particular ratio between the number of windings of a primary coil and a secondary coil, and for a certain fixed value of voltage input to the primary coil, some higher or lower fixed value of voltage output can be obtained from the secondary coil. In addition, however, the elements must have the ability to change the phases of their output in order to establish the direction of the correcting control signals. In applying this principle to error sensing, it is necessary for the secondary coil output to be of a variable nature, and in order to derive this the basic iron core structure is arranged in two parts, one part being fixed while the position of the other part is variable. Some examples of the methods commonly adopted are the 'E' and 'I' method; the moving vane method; and the method of synchronous transmission.

E and I bar sensors

An example of this type of sensor is illustrated in fig. 4.1. The centre limb of the fixed E-shaped core is wound with a primary coil supplied with alternating current at the required level, while the two outer limbs are wound with secondary coils connected in series opposition. The I bar is pivoted at its centre, and is rotated by the attitude sensing element, in this case of the gyroscopic type, so that the bar varies the air gaps between it and the outer limbs of the E-shaped core. When the I bar is in its neutral position, the air gaps are equal, an equal magnetic flux flows in each limb of the E-shaped core, thereby inducing equal and opposite voltages in the secondary coils; the output from the coils is therefore zero.

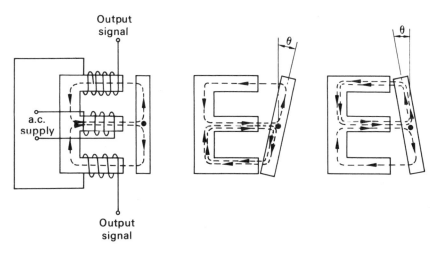

Fig. 4.1 E and I bar sensor

When the attitude sensing element detects a change in attitude (either as a result of disturbance of the aircraft or by injection of a required attitude change command signal) the I bar is deflected through a small angle such that the air gaps will no longer be equal, and the reluctance of the magnetic circuit will change. The flux in one outer limb of the E core will increase, while the flux in the other decreases; thus, there will be corresponding changes in the voltages induced in the secondary coils, and an output signal voltage will be produced. The greater the I bar deflection, the greater will be the signal voltages, and since the secondary coils are wound in opposition the voltage will be either in-phase or out-of-phase with respect to the input voltage to the primary coil, depending on the direction in which the I bar is deflected. The phase and magnitude of the signal are directly proportional to the direction and magnitude of the detected attitude change; thus, by amplifying the signal and feeding it to a servomotor, an appropriate flight control surface can be moved either to correct a disturbance or to manoeuvre the aircraft in response to an attitude change command. To ensure that the servomotor provides the required amount of control surface displacement, or runs at a rate proportional to that of a disturbance as the case may be, a feedback signal is applied to the control loop to oppose the error voltage signal; (some typical methods adopted for the generation of feedback are described in chapter 7).

Moving vane method

This is adopted in some types of flight control system in which the inductive pick-off elements are actuated by the vertical gyroscope of a steering horizon indicator, an example being one of the flight director/autopilot systems manufactured by Edo-Aire Mitchell.

Two pick-off elements are employed, and they each consist of a moving vane and a fixed coil assembly as shown schematically in fig. 4.2. One element has its vane mounted on the inner gimbal ring of the gyroscope, and therefore senses pitch attitude changes, while the vane of the second element is mounted on the outer gimbal ring, and senses changes in roll attitude.

A square-wave alternating voltage is applied to coils 1 and 3 of each fixed coil assembly, the voltages being 180° out-of-phase. In the level flight attitude (diagram *a*) the vanes of both elements are centred over the number 2 coils, and since in this position there is equal electro-magnetic coupling between coils 1 and 3, no voltage is induced in coil 2 and no command signal will be applied to the computer/amplifier.

When a change in aircraft attitude occurs about one or other of the vertical gyroscope axes, there will be relative movement between the vane and coil assembly of the relevant pick-off element. Thus, assuming that movement causes the vane to be centred between coils 2 and 3 (diagram *b*) the inductance will be increased and a square-wave voltage will be induced in coil 2, and which is in phase with the input to coil 3. A command signal will therefore, be applied to the computer/amplifier. Movement of the vane towards coil 1 (diagram *c*) results in a similar response except that the voltage induced in coil 2 is in phase with the inputs to coil 1.

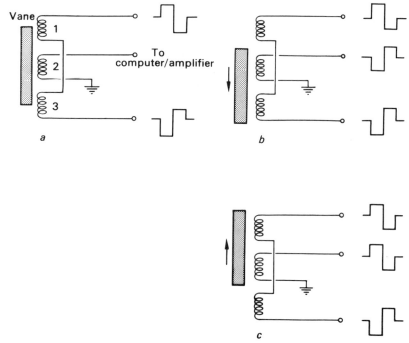

Fig. 4.2 Moving-vane pick-off element

Synchronous transmission systems

In many automatic flight control systems, the detection of error signals is accomplished by self-synchronous inductive devices which are usually classified under the generic term *synchro*. They are divided into four main groups according to their function: (i) torque synchros, (ii) control synchros, (iii) differential synchros and (iv) resolver synchros.

Torque synchros

These are the simplest form of synchro and are used for the transmission of angular position information by means of induced signals, and for the reproduction of this information by the position of a shaft at an output or receiver element. A typical application of torque synchros is in flight instrument systems.

A torque synchro system is comprised of two electrically similar units interconnected as shown in fig. 4.3, and by convention one is designated the transmitter (TX) and the other the receiver (TR). Each unit consists of a rotor carrying a winding, and concentrically mounted in a stator carrying three windings the axes of which are 120° apart. The principal physical differences between the TX and the TR are that the

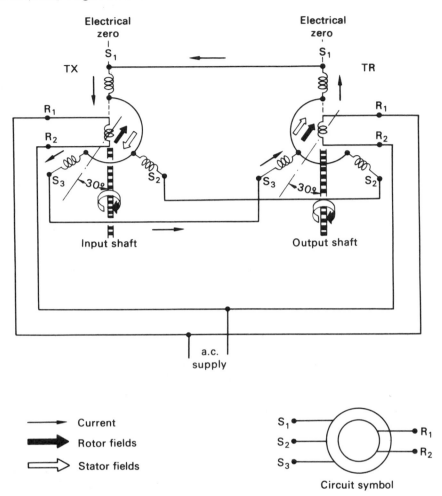

Fig. 4.3 Torque synchro system

rotor of the TX is mechanically coupled to an input shaft, while the TR rotor is free to rotate. The rotor windings are connected to a source of single-phase alternating current supply, and the corresponding stator connections are joined together by transmission lines. A similarity between these connection arrangements and a conventional transformer may also be noted; the rotors corresponding to primary windings and the stators to secondary windings.

When the rotors are aligned with their respective stators in the position indicated they are said to be at 'electrical zero'; this refers to the reference angle standardised for synchros at which a given set of stator voltages will be produced, and by this convention enables replacement synchros to be matched to each other. Other positions are measured in degrees increasing in an anti-clockwise direction when viewed from the output shaft end of the unit. With power applied to the rotors the alternating flux set up will, by transformer action, induce certain voltages in the stator coils, the voltage values being governed, as in any transformer, by the ratio of the number of turns of the rotor (primary) and stator (secondary) coils.

When the rotors are at 'null', the induced voltages will be equal and opposite; therefore, no current flows in the stator coils and so there are no magnetic fields produced to cause rotation of the rotor of TR. However, when the rotor of TX is turned, say, through an angle of 30° an imbalance occurs between the voltages induced in the stator coils, causing current to flow in the stator coils and transmission lines. The currents are greatest in the circuit where voltage imbalance is greatest, and their effect is to produce resultant magnetic fields which exert torques to turn the rotor of TR to the same position as that of TX. As the TR rotor continues to turn, the misalignment, voltage imbalance and currents decrease until the 30° position is reached and no further torque is exerted on the rotor.

Control synchros

Control synchros differ from torque synchros in that their function is to produce an error voltage signal in the receiving element, as opposed to the production of a rotor torque. Since this error signal is an indication of misalignment between an input and an output, control synchros are more widely used as attitude error detectors which, as we learned earlier, form part of closed-loop servo control systems.

The interconnection of the two elements of a control synchro system as applied to a gyroscopic attitude sensing element, is shown in fig. 4.4. By convention, the transmitter is designated as CX, and the receiver designated as a control transformer CT. The CX is similar to a torque transmitter, and from the diagram it will be noted that the alternating current supply is connected to the CX rotor only. The CT rotor is not energised since it acts merely as an inductive winding for detecting the phase and magnitude of error signal voltages which are supplied to an amplifier. The amplified signals are then fed to a two-phase motor which is mechanically coupled to the CT rotor. Another difference to be noted is that a control synchro system is at electrical zero when the rotor of CT is at 90° with respect to the CX rotor.

In practical applications, the transmitters are located about the appropriate axes of the attitude sensing element, for example, the pitch and roll axes of a vertical reference unit, the rotors being secured to the gimbal rings. Thus, assuming that a disturbance about the pitch axis takes place, the stator of the pitch CX will rotate about the

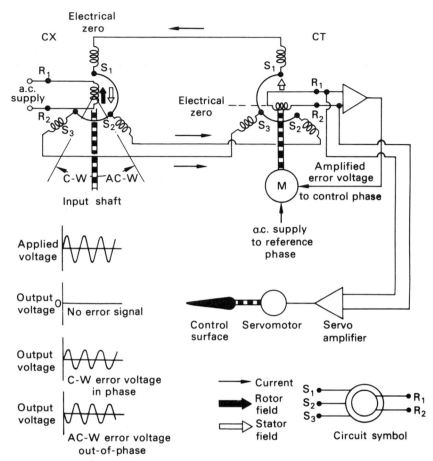

Fig. 4.4 Control synchro system

stabilised rotor through a certain angle and the resultant flux in the CT stator will be displaced from its datum point by the same angle, and relative to the CT rotor position at that instant. An error voltage is therefore induced in the rotor, the phase and magnitude of the voltage depending on the direction of CX rotor rotation and on the degree of misalignment between it and the CT rotor. The error voltage is then amplified and fed to the control phase of the motor, the other phase being continuously supplied with alternating current. Since the control phase voltage of a two-phase motor can either lead or lag the reference phase voltage, the phase of the error voltage will determine the direction in which the motor will rotate, and its magnitude will determine its speed of rotation. As the motor rotates, it turns the rotor of the CT in the appropriate direction, thereby reducing its displacement relative to the CX rotor. Rotation continues until both rotors are in alignment (bearing in mind of course that the electrical zero points are at 90° from each other), at which position no further error voltage is induced.

Following a disturbance of the type considered in this example, it is necessary for the elevator to be displaced in order to return the aircraft to its normal flight attitude. This is accomplished by also applying the error voltage induced in the CT, to the power output section of the servo control channel loop. Thus, as can also be seen from fig. 4.4, the error voltage is applied to a servo amplifier which increases the magnitude of the voltage sufficient to drive the servomotor and so proportionately displace the elevators in the appropriate direction, until there is no further error. As the aircraft returns to its normal flight attitude, the change is again sensed by the vertical reference unit and the pitch CX, but the error voltage induced is now opposite in phase to that of the original displacement. Thus, the control synchro and pitch servo control systems are operated in the same manner as that described but in the opposite direction.

Differential synchros

In some cases, it is necessary to detect and transmit error signals representative of two angular positions, and in such a manner that the receiver element of a synchro system will indicate the difference or the sum of the two angles. This is achieved by introducing a third synchro into either a torque or control system, and using it as a differential transmitter. Unlike TX or CX synchros, a differential transmitter (designated TDX or CDX) has an identically wound stator and rotor interconnected as shown in fig. 4.5.

As an illustration of the operation, we may consider the application of a differential transmitter to a torque synchro system at varying angular inputs as indicated in fig. 4.5. At *a* the TX rotor is shown rotated clockwise through 60° while the rotor of TDX remains at electrical zero; all the magnetic fields rotate, and the rotor of TR takes up the same angular position as the rotor of TX. If now the TX rotor remains at electrical zero, and the TDX rotor is rotated clockwise through 15°, say, the fields of both synchros remain in the electrical zero position because their position is determined by the orientation of the TX rotor (diagram *b*). However, a 15° clockwise rotation of the TDX rotor without a change in the position of its field is equivalent to moving the rotor field 15° anti-clockwise while leaving the rotor at electrical zero. This relative angular change is duplicated in the stator of TR and so its rotor will align itself with the field, i.e. for a 15° clockwise rotation of the TDX rotor, the TR rotor will rotate 15° anti-clockwise.

Assume now that the TX rotor is rotated through 60° clockwise, and

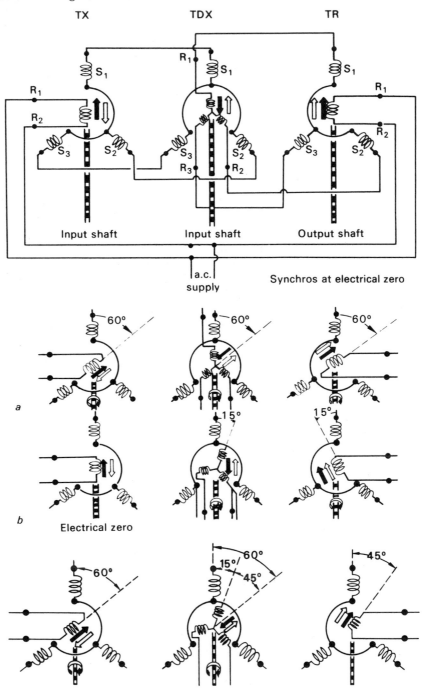

Fig. 4.5 Differential synchro in torque synchro system

Rotor fields

Stator fields

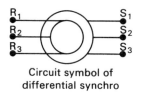

R_1 S_1
R_2 S_2
R_3 S_3

Circuit symbol of
differential synchro

Fig. 4.5 (*contd.*)

the TDX rotor through 15° clockwise, then because the TR rotor will rotate 15° anti-clockwise its final angular movement will be equal to the difference between the two input angles, i.e. it will turn through 45° (diagram *c*). The differential effect is of course reversed when the TDX rotor is rotated in the opposite direction to the TX rotor, so that the TR rotor rotates through an angle equal to the sum of the two input angles. By reversing pairs of leads either between TX and TDX, or between TDX and TR, any one of the rotors can be made to assume a position equal to the sum or the difference of the angular positions of the other rotors.

In the same way that differential transmitter synchros can be used in torque synchro systems, they can be used in systems utilising control synchros to transmit control signal information on the sum or difference of two angles. The basic arrangement is shown in fig. 4.6.

Resolver synchros

The function of resolver synchros (designated RS) is to convert alternating voltages, which represent the cartesian coordinates of a point, into a shaft position, and a voltage, which together represent the polar coordinates of that point. They may also be used in the reverse manner for voltage conversion from polar to cartesian coordinates. A vector representing an alternating voltage can be defined in terms of the vector length (see fig. 4.7) and the angle it makes with the X axis; these are the polar coordinates of the vector. The vector **r** can also be defined in terms of x and y where $x = \mathbf{r} \cos \theta$ and $y = \mathbf{r} \sin \theta$; these expressions are the cartesian coordinates of the vector.

A typical arrangement of an RS for conversion from polar to cartesian coordinates is shown in fig. 4.8, and from this it will be noted that the stator and rotor each have two windings arranged in phase quadrature, thus providing an eight-terminal synchro. An alternating voltage is applied to the rotor winding $R_1 - R_2$, and the magnitude of this voltage, together with the angle through which the rotor is turned, represent the polar coordinates. In this application, the second winding is unused, and as is usual in such cases, it is short-circuited to improve the accuracy of the RS and to limit the spurious response.

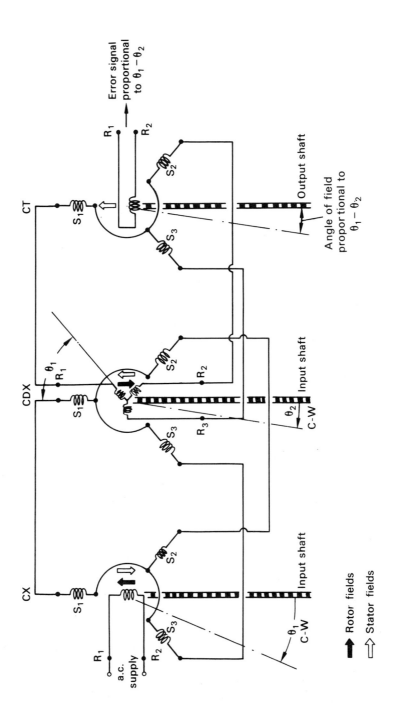

Fig. 4.6 Differential synchro in control synchro system

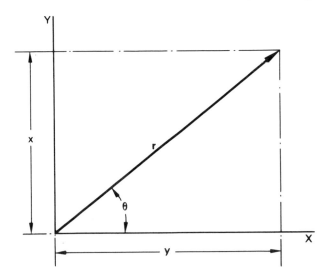

Fig. 4.7 Cartesian coordinates of a point

In the position shown, the alternating flux produced by the current through rotor winding R_1-R_2, links with both stator windings, but since the rotor winding is aligned only with S_1-S_2, then maximum voltage will be induced in this winding. Winding S_3-S_4 is in phase quadrature so no voltage is induced in it. When the rotor is rotated at a constant speed it will induce voltages in both stator windings, the voltages varying sinusoidally. The voltage across that stator winding which is aligned with the rotor at electrical zero will be a maximum at that position and will fall to zero after rotor displacement of 90°; this voltage is therefore a measure of the cosine of the displacement. The voltage is in phase with the voltage applied to R_1-R_2 during the first 90° of displacement, and in anti-phase from 90° to 270°, finally rising from zero at 270° to maximum in-phase at 360°. Any angular displacement can therefore be identified by the amplitude and phase of the induced stator voltages. At electrical zero, stator winding S_3-S_4 will have zero voltage induced in it, but at 90° displacement of rotor winding R_1-R_2, maximum in-phase voltage will be induced and will vary sinusoidally throughout 360°; thus, the S_3-S_4 voltage is directly proportional to the sine of the rotor displacement. The phase depends on the angle of displacement, any angle being identified by the amplitude and phase of the voltages induced in stator winding S_3-S_4. The sum of the outputs from both stators, i.e. $\mathbf{r}\cos\theta$ plus $\mathbf{r}\sin\theta$, therefore defines in cartesian coordinates the input voltage and rotor rotation.

Fig. 4.9 illustrates an arrangement whereby cartesian coordinates may be converted to polar coordinates. An alternating voltage $V_x=\mathbf{r}\cos\theta$ is

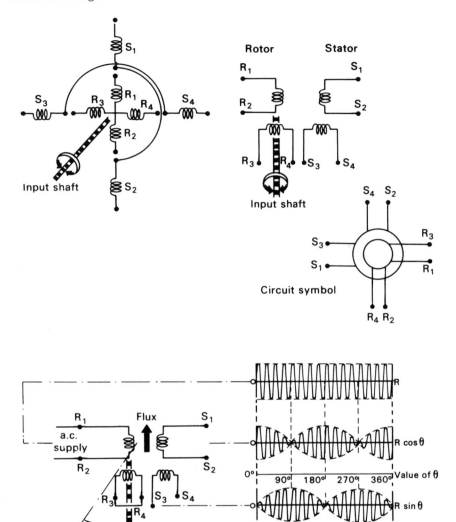

Fig. 4.8 Resolver synchro

applied to the cosine stator winding S_1-S_2, while a voltage $V_y = \mathbf{r} \sin \theta$ is applied to the sine stator winding S_3-S_4. An alternating flux representing cartesian coordinates is therefore produced inside the complete stator. One of the rotor windings, in this case R_1-R_2, is connected to an amplifier and in the position shown it will have maximum voltage induced in it; this voltage will be applied to the amplifier. The output from the amplifier is applied to a servomotor which is mechanically coupled to a load and to the rotor. When the rotor is

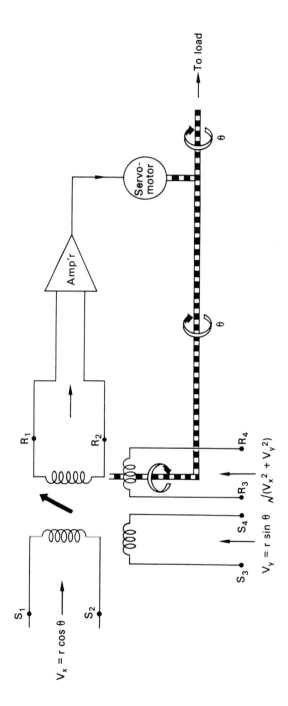

Fig. 4.9 Conversion of cartesian coordinates to polar coordinates

turned through 90° the induced voltage in winding R_1-R_2, reduces to zero and the servomotor will stop. The rotor winding R_3-R_4 will now be aligned with the stator flux, and a voltage will be induced in it which is proportional to the amplitude of the alternating flux as represented by the vector **r**, i.e. a voltage proportional to $\sqrt{(V_x^2+V_y^2}.)$ This voltage together with the angular position of the rotor therefore represents an output in terms of the polar coordinates.

A typical example of RS application to a control channel of an automatic flight control system is shown in fig. 4.10. In this case, the control system is one employing rate gyroscopes and a vertical gyroscope, for attitude sensing, and the resolver performs the function of converting cartesian coordinates to polar coordinates in order to establish a true pitch rate (movement of an aircraft about a true horizontal axis) for pitch stabilisation. When the aircraft turns, the outputs from the pitch and roll rate gyroscopes contain a rate-of-change-of-heading component, and the output from the yaw rate gyroscope contains a rate-of-change-of-elevation component. The effect of the component in the pitch rate signal is to produce a continuous pitch-down signal; the elevation rate component is nullified by the yaw channel circuit. If, therefore, the pitch and yaw rate signals can be resolved with respect to the roll rate then the true pitch rate of the aircraft during turns can be determined.

The roll attitude signal is fed to the stator of a CT synchro and this establishes an error signal representing the roll angle, in the rotor. After amplification, the signal is applied to the control winding of a motor, the shaft of which is mechanically coupled to the CT rotor and to the RS rotor. The motor therefore rotates the CT rotor to reduce the error signal to zero (generally termed datum chasing) and also rotates the RS rotor to a position which mechanically represents the roll angle at that instant. The RS stator is electrically connected to the pitch rate signal and yaw rate signal amplifier, so that during turns, two rate signals are supplied to the stator which have a sine/cosine relationship, and produce a resultant error signal with respect to the rotor, the signal representing the true pitch rate. The true pitch rate signal output from RS is applied to a pitch servo amplifier which produces the required control signal for operating the elevator servomotor so as to correct for the nose-down pitch rate signal component produced during turns.

Versine generator

In some types of automatic flight control system, the correction of the tendency of an aircraft to drop its nose during turns is accomplished by a network known as a versine generator which is operated by signals from the pitch and roll attitude detector transmitter (CX) synchros attached to a vertical gyroscope. The ciruit arrangement is shown in fig. 4.11 from which it will also be noted that this is another example of

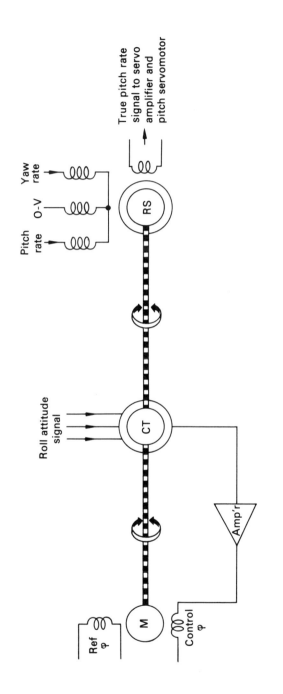

Fig. 4.10 Resolver synchro application

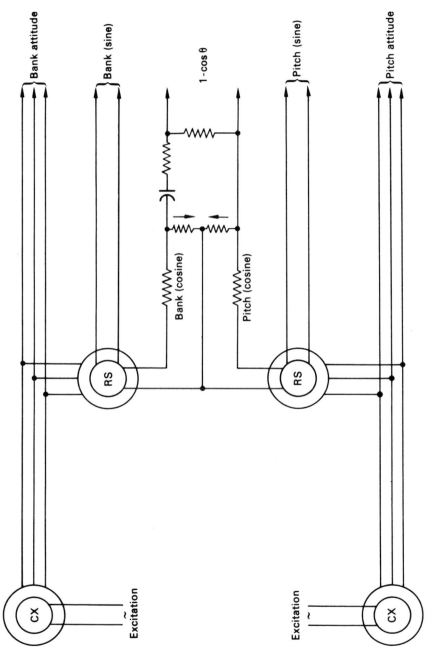

Fig. 4.11 Versine generator

resolver synchro (RS) application. The signals from each CX are supplied to the RS stators, and as the rotor windings are in phase quadrature, the signals induced in them are the sine and cosine of the transmitted attitude signals. The pitch and roll sine signals are fed to the appropriate corrective control channels, while the cosine signals are fed to a network which places them in opposition. At zero pitch and roll angles, the cosine of each angle is unity and, being in opposition, the output to the pitch channel is zero. At some angle of roll the cosine of the angle decreases, while that of the pitch angle remains substantially the same, no movement in pitch having taken place. The opposing signals in this condition are, therefore, cosine of pitch angle equal to unity, and cosine of roll angle less than unity; thus, the resulting signal is $1 - \cos \theta$, where θ is the roll angle in degrees, and corresponds to the trigonometric function of an angle, known as the versine. The corresponding versine signal is fed to the pitch servo channel to provide the required nose-up displacement during turns. Since the cosine of the roll angle decreases as the angle increases, the versine signal will also increase and so result in greater nose-up displacement.

Acceleration and sideslip sensors

The variable transformer principle described on page 102 is also applied to sensors designed for sensing accelerations, sideslip and for the monitoring of sustained pitch attitude and heading changes (see also page 128) particularly those which may be outside the limiting threshold sensitivity of gyroscopic elements. In each case, the differences relate principally to the manner in which deflection of the moving part of the element takes place.

Fig. 4.12 shows how the E and I bar method is applied to the sensing of accelerations. The I bar constitutes the mass which is suspended adjacent to the E bar by two springs. Under constant velocity conditions, the I bar remains centred, and no signal is induced in the output coil. When the unit is accelerated or decelerated, the I bar tends to remain at rest resulting in relative movement between it and the E bar, and in the induction of a signal voltage in the manner already described. After processing by the appropriate computer/amplifier, the signal is supplied to the relevant servomotor which then displaces its flight control surface to correct for the change in attitude.

The location of acceleration tranducers with respect to the three axes of an aircraft is also shown in fig. 4.12. In some aircraft systems, each axis is assigned a pair of transducers, which are spaced apart and are differentially connected (electrically) so that the resultant signal

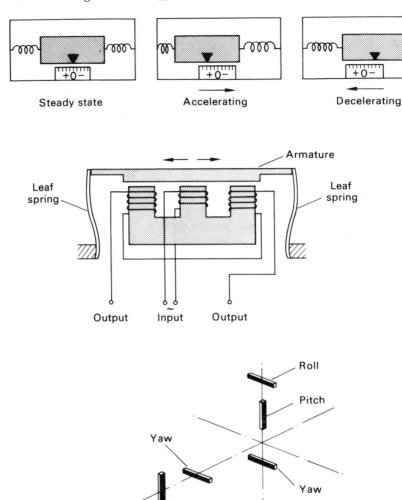

Steady state

Accelerating

Decelerating

Armature

Leaf spring

Leaf spring

Output

Input

Output

Roll

Pitch

Yaw

Yaw

Forward

Pitch

Roll

Fig. 4.12 Acceleration transducer principle

generated by a pair is a measure of angular acceleration about the appropriate reference axis. Again, in some systems it may be usual to have only one sensor for sensing vertical acceleration, and to utilise the output for stabilising flight control system operation in the vertical and airspeed hold modes.

In a co-ordinated turn, i.e. one in which the angle of roll is correct for a selected rate of turn, the vertical (gravitational) force, and the lateral (centrifugal) force are in balance, and they can be resolved into a vector perpendicular to the aircraft's lateral axis; this is known as the dynamic vertical. If, however, there is lack of co-ordination, then the resulting imbalance of forces will cause the aircraft to either slip or skid. The primary attitude sensing elements of an automatic flight control system are unable to detect slip or skid since movement of the aircraft causes bodily displacement of the stabilised axes of the elements, in other words aircraft movement would no longer be relative to the axes. This can be overcome by providing monitoring devices capable of sensing the imbalance of forces and of producing signals which can be applied to the rudder servo control channel and thereby restore co-ordination.

One such device, known as a dynamic vertical sensor, is shown in fig. 4.13. It is comprised of a pendulum-actuated synchro transmitter the axis of which is aligned with the fore-and-aft axis of the aircraft,

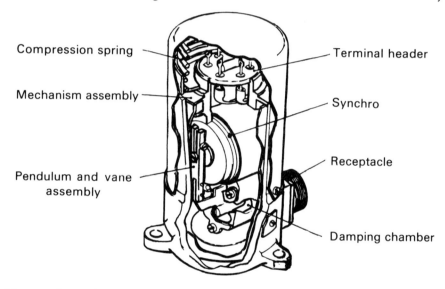

Compression spring

Mechanism assembly

Pendulum and vane assembly

Terminal header

Synchro

Receptacle

Damping chamber

Fig. 4.13 Dynamic vertical sensor

and so restricting displacement of the pendulum to the athwartships axis direction only. Oil damping is provided to prevent the pendulum from being affected by transient oscillations and vibration. In a co-ordinated turn, the pendulum is aligned with the dynamic vertical, and no output signal is produced in the synchro stator. If however, the pendulum is displaced as a result of a slip or skid, the synchro rotor will also be displaced to induce a proportional signal in the stator. The signal is then amplified and supplied to the rudder servo control channel, the output of which will displace the rudder causing it to co-ordinate the turn.

An example of a sensor designed for monitoring attitude changes less than those which a primary attitude sensing device is capable of detecting, is shown in fig. 4.14. It is known as a pendulum monitor and it is used in a type of control system employing rate gyroscopes. It detects long-term attitude changes by responding to the actual displacement of an aircraft, rather than the rate of disturbance, and corrects the changes by supplying signals to the servo control channel in which it is connected. The monitor may also be used for sideslip sensing.

The monitor consists of a pendulum frame pivoted about a core which is wound with a primary and a secondary coil at right angles to each other. When the frame is in its zero position, the alternating current in the primary winding produces a flux in the upper and lower parts of the core, and since the flux does not cut the secondary winding, no voltage is induced in it. When a loss of attitude datum occurs, the monitor core is tilted one way or the other, and this creates a displacement between it and the pendulum frame, and distortion of the primary flux (diagram *b*). The distorted flux cuts the secondary coil and induces in it a voltage which is proportional to the angle of displacement. The phase of the secondary voltage depends on the direction of flux distortion, and this, in turn, depends on the direction in which the monitor is displaced.

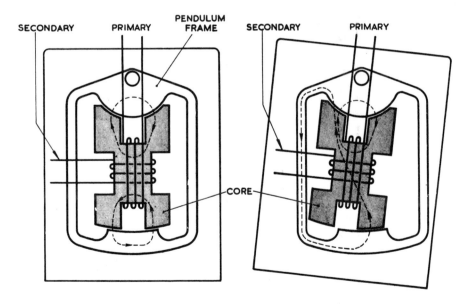

Fig. 4.14 Pendulum monitor

5
Command Signal Processing

The signals produced by error signal sensors, in whatever form the sensors may take, cannot be applied directly to their associated servomotors for the principal reasons that further computation of signals is necessary particularly when outer loop control is adopted (see chapter 6), and in terms of power capability they are not strong enough to cope with the aerodynamic loads acting on the control surfaces. Therefore, in any one flight control system it is necessary to incorporate within the corresponding servo control loops a signal processing system having some, or all, of the following functions:

(i) Differentiating, e.g. deriving simulated rate information from a vertical gyroscope controlled signal sensor.

(ii) Demodulating, i.e. converting a.c. error signals into d.c. control signals which have the same phase relationship.

(iii) Integrating to obtain simulated attitude information or to correct any sustained attitude errors.

(iv) Amplifying to increase sensor signals to a level high enough to operate the servomotors.

(v) Limiting to ensure that certain parameter changes are kept within prescribed limits.

(vi) Signal shaping to adapt system response to suit the handling qualities or flight path of an aircraft.

(vii) Programming to produce a precise manoeuvre, e.g. when selecting a particular outer loop control mode.

The methods adopted for performing the foregoing functions are varied and, in common with the other elements which make up any one complete control system, such methods are governed by system design and how it relates to the handling characteristics of various types of aircraft. Within the confines of this chapter, therefore, it is not possible to go into any great detail of the individual control channel configurations. There is, however, a basic similarity between the requirements for, and the applications of, signal processing elements, and the fundamentals of purpose and operation may be understood with the aid of the block diagram of fig. 5.1. Although the diagram is based on an aileron servo-control channel of a particular type of flight control system, it may nevertheless be considered generally representative.

When a turn has been demanded either through the medium of the compass system, the turn controller, or by the VOR or Localiser navigation receivers, a corresponding roll attitude error signal is determined by summing the values of the demanded roll attitude signal and the signal corresponding to the existing attitude; the latter signal is sensed by the roll sensing element of the vertical reference unit. Summation takes place in this case at point 'A' and the error signal produced is fed into the servo-control loop at point 'B'. Also at this point, a signal from a roll rate gyroscope sensing element is fed in to establish a turn rate for the demand, and to prevent over-controlling. This is an example of the use of a displacement gyroscope and rate gyroscope in combination (see page 90). Since the demanded roll attitude requires the ailerons to be displaced from their existing position, a position comparison process is also necessary to compute the error signal for servomotor operation. This is effected at the summing point 'C' to which is supplied what may be termed an 'existing position' feedback signal. The purpose of this signal is to correct for non-linearities between the servomotor and the aileron system. The resulting difference signal is then applied to a discriminator, or pre-amplifier module, which removes quadrature and harmonic voltages and also increases the gain of the servo-control loop, thereby improving its reponse to signals demanding only small changes in aileron position. At the output side of the discriminator, and at summing point 'D', a rate feedback signal from the servomotor tachogenerator, is injected to back-off the demand signal and so provide damping and servo-loop stability. The combined signal is therefore the one required to drive the servomotor to the demanded position, but in order to do this the signal must pass through a further stage of amplification and, as in all types of flight control systems, this is accomplished by means of a servo-amplifier.

Servo-amplifiers may be designed to be of either d.c. or a.c. type depending on the power source for which servomotors themselves have been designed. In the system represented in fig. 5.1, the servomotors

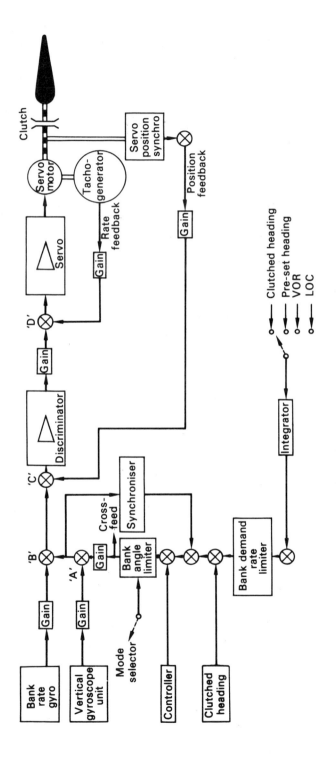

Fig. 5.1 Signal processing

are of the a.c. type, and the drive signals to them are amplified by saturable reactors, or magnetic amplifiers, which require d.c. for controlling the amplification. The d.c. is obtained by converting the combined signal from summing point 'C' through a conversion process known as demodulation. The saturable reactor and demodulator amplifier are two modular 'card' assemblies electrically interconnected within the servo-amplifier.

The combined demand signal is fed to the demodulator input, and after it has been phase related to a.c. reference signals, it is converted to a d.c. control signal voltage having a polarity directly related to the phase of the a.c. demand signal. The d.c. signal is then fed to the control windings of a bridge-type saturable reactor so as to control the magnetic saturation of its cores and, therefore, to control the inductive reactance of the bridge. The signal is also fed to a trim indicator to indicate that a demand signal is in the servo-control loop (see page 187).

The reactor has two cores with windings connected to form an impedance bridge circuit which is supplied with a.c. at some pre-set value, e.g. 115 volts. A set of d.c. control windings is wound on each core so that when there is no demand signal to the demodulator the current flowing through both windings is equal, the bridge remains in balance, and there is no output from the reactor. When a demand signal is fed to the demodulator, then, as its d.c. output signal to the reactor will have a polarity related to the phase of the demand signal, a difference between the currents flowing through the control windings will be established, thereby unbalancing the bridge. Since this changes the balance between inductive reactances, the reactor output is an amplified a.c. control signal which is then supplied to the servomotor. In the system considered, the servomotor is of the two-phase induction type, and the control signal is supplied to the variable-phase winding. The direction of motor rotation is governed by the phase angle between the current flowing in the variable-phase winding, and that in the fixed-phase winding, the motor rotating clockwise or anti-clockwise depending on whether the variable-phase lags or leads the fixed-phase which is supplied from the main power source. A capacitor is inserted across the input to the servomotor to provide phase adjustment to the variable-phase current and this will always maintain a phase angle (whether lagging or leading) relative to the fixed-phase, thus maintaining rotation of the servomotor in the direction demanded by the original input signal. Stabilising of the servo control loop is effected by feeding back part of the variable-phase signals to the demodulator amplifier via a phase-shifting network, which corrects for phase differences between the demodulator amplifier input and saturable reactor output.

When the difference between demanded and existing attitude is zero, there is then no further input to the servo-amplifier, the servo-motor ceases to rotate, and the control surfaces (ailerons in this case) take up the position required to satisfy the demanded attitude change. Oscillations and 'hunting' of the servomotor about the zero signal point are prevented by supplying rate feedback signals from the servomotor tachogenerator (see page 176).

Referring to fig. 5.1 it will be noted that a servo-control channel is also dependent on other elements, the signals from which are utilised for the improvement of system response to commanded attitude changes and ultimate control capability. The functions of these elements, and brief details of their operating fundamentals are given in the following paragraphs.

Limiting

Under automatically controlled flight conditions, it is necessary to monitor what is generally termed the 'authority' of the control system, notably in respect of the roll and pitch channels; in other words, limits must be placed on demanded control signals to prevent excessive attitude changes and harsh manoeuvring.

In the roll control channel shown in fig. 5.1 it will be noted that there are two limiting elements in the signal processing chain: a roll demand rate limiter, and a roll demand limiter. The rate limiter limits the rate of change of demand signals to some selected value, e.g. 5 degrees/second, so as to 'soften' aileron displacements and prevent harsh rolling of the aircraft. Signal processing through the limiter network is such that it imposes a specific time constant on the roll demand signal. The roll demand limiter controls the roll angle authority of the control system, the limit which the circuit is actually capable of being dependent on the control mode selected. Limits are accurately pre-set by potentiometers, and when the control channel is operating in the appropriate mode they are controlled by a d.c. bias signal applied to limiting diodes within the limiter module.

The roll demand rate limiter consists of a limiting demodulator, a simple d.c. integrator, and a 400 Hz modulator stage with overall unity feedback. As already mentioned, it imposes lag on the roll demand signal with a specific time constant; in this example the constant is about 10 seconds.

The output from the limiter module is summed with signals from the appropriate outer loop elements, and fed into the servo-control signal chain at summing points 'A' and 'B'. In addition, the limiter output is crossfed to the rudder control channel to provide co-ordination of the turn resulting from the displacement of the ailerons.

Synchronising

The necessity for synchronising has already been explained in chapter 2, and fig. 5.1 shows the interconnection of a synchronising element within the roll demand signal chain. When the flight control system is not engaged, and the aircraft is in a turn, the combined signal outputs from the vertical gyroscope sensing element and roll angle limiting networks are fed as an input to the synchronising element. The element is a low-pass filter which reproduces the combined signal but with a time lag. It also inverts the phasing of the signal and feeds it back into the signal chain with a high negative gain in order to reduce the combined signal to zero. Thus, a zero roll angle is established as the reference for the attitude detecting element, i.e. the vertical gyroscope, prior to engagement. On engaging the control system, the relay in the engage interlock circuit (see also page 61) is energised and short-circuits the input to the synchroniser. After a short time delay (10 seconds is typical) the demand signal stored in the synchroniser decays, thereby leaving the roll attitude signal from the vertical gyroscope sensing element to control the aircraft to zero roll angle, and because synchronism is now established between the attitude signal and heading error signal from the compass system the aircraft will be levelled out smoothly on to the heading existing at the time of engagement. Without synchronisation, the aircraft would rapidly level out on to an incorrect heading, and a heading error signal would then replace the original bank attitude signal.

Integration

Under certain flight conditions, e.g. crosswind conditions (see page 153), changing load conditions, etc., it is possible for sustained or recurring displacements from automatically stabilised references to occur, thereby setting up errors. A persistent displacement error may exist at such a low level that it will not actuate the associated servo-control channel to cause corrective action, and if permitted to remain the displacement error will be further increased.

Various methods may be adopted to correct the errors, and whether any one of them is applied depends on the design requirements of a particular automatic flight control system. The pendulum monitor already described on page 122 is a method adopted in one system, but in a majority of cases the principle of signal integration is applied as an error correction technique in any one selected mode of control system operation. The displacement error condition is integrated with the time that the displacement exists, and the resultant integration signal

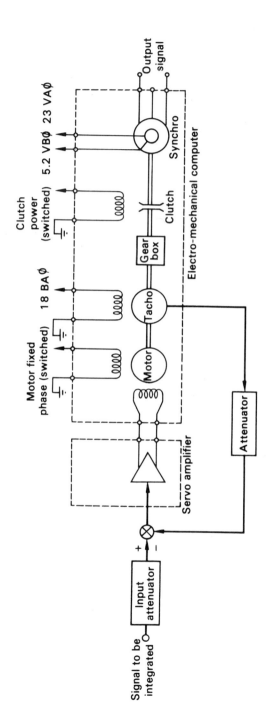

Fig. 5.2 Integrator unit

voltage is developed in a servo-loop added to the basic servo-control system. The principal elements of a loop adopted in the roll control channel shown in fig. 5.1 are: a servo amplifier to which the error signal is supplied, and an electro-mechanical computer unit; their interconnection is schematically illustrated in fig. 5.2.

The computer unit consists of a two-phase induction motor, a tachogenerator, a high reduction gear train, an electro-magnetic clutch, and a synchro control transformer (CT). The control phase of the motor is supplied by the output from the servo-amplifier; thus, whenever there is an error signal, the motor is operated and drives the tachogenerator, and by means of the gear train and energised clutch it also positions the rotor of the CT. The signal output from the CT is then applied to the amplifier of the basic servo-control system, thereby adding to its command signal input. The tachogenerator produces a signal proportional to the motor speed, and since this signal is fed back to the servo-amplifier, it ensures that the motor runs at a speed determined by the input signal level and the attenuation of the rate feedback signal. The CT output signal builds up at a slow rate, and through the basic servo-control system it provides increased correction until the displacement error is zeroed. When this occurs, there is no longer an input voltage to the amplifier of the integrator unit and the motor ceases to rotate. The integrator unit is so designed that under certain modes of operation, e.g. when flying through the 'cone of confusion' in the VOR mode (see page 156) the CT output signal is stored, and the integrator acts as a memory device. When the clutch is de-energised (by dis-engaging the automatic control system) the CT rotor is spring-returned to its 'null' position.

The integrator time constant is defined as the time taken for the output voltage to rise to the same value as the input voltage. It varies depending on the particular control channel to which it is applied, and on the outer loop control mode selected. For example, in the roll control channel shown in fig. 5.1, the time constant in the pre-set heading mode is 50 seconds, while in either the VOR or Localiser mode it is 388 seconds and 43 seconds respectively. The basic time constant is determined by the sensitivities of the CT and tachogenerator, the attenuation of the rate feedback signal, and the gear ratio between the tachogenerator and CT.

6
Outer Loop Control

In addition to peforming the primary function of stabilisation, an automatic flight control system can also be developed to perform the tasks of modifying the stabilised attitude of an aircraft by computing the necessary manoeuvres from inputs of such raw data as airspeed, altitude, magnetic heading, interception of radio beams from ground-based aids, etc. Such data inputs constitute outer loop control (see fig. 6.1), the number of inputs serving as an indication of the progressive development of automatic flight from the basic single-axis wing-levelling type of autopilot to the highly sohpisticated flight guidance systems used in many present-day transport aircraft. The provision of raw data inputs relevant to a particular flight path is referred to as 'coupling' or as a 'mode of operation', the selection of each mode being made by the pilot via appropriate control panel switching devices. Other terms commonly used in connection with operating modes are: 'hold', 'lock' and 'capture'; for example, an aircraft flying automatically at a selected altitude is said to be in the 'altitude hold' or 'height lock' mode. The term 'capture' relates principally to modes associated with the selection and interception of beams from ground-based radio navigation aids; for example, 'glide slope capture'.

In some cases, mode switching is automatic; thus, to switch from intercepting a beam or a heading to tracking the beam on reaching it, a beam sensor is installed. This device senses beam deviation and switches modes automatically when the aircraft flies into the beam. Glide slope capture can also take place automatically, in this case the pitch control channel is switched from 'altitude hold' mode to glide slope track when the aircraft flies into the glide slope beam.

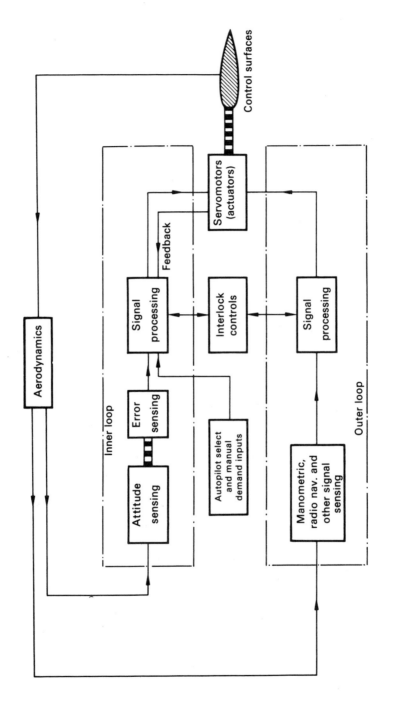

Fig. 6.1 Inner loop stabilisation and outer loop control

Pitch axis	Roll axis
Manometric or air data:	Heading select and hold
Altitude select and hold	
Vertical speed	Bank hold
Airspeed select and hold	
Mach hold	Radio navigation:
	VOR
Pitch hold	Back beam
Pitch trim	Area navigation:
	Doppler
Turbulence penetration	Inertial
Vertical navigation	

Instrument Landing System

Glide slope	Localiser

Autoland

Approach	Runway align
Flare	Roll out

Control Wheel Steering

The raw data is supplied from sensors which convert the data into appropriate electrical signals that can be mixed in with inner control loop signal data to produce the changes to the aircraft's flight path. The traditional raw data instrument displays are used by the pilot for monitoring, and programming management. Outer loop control modes which may be incorporated in a control system are listed in the table above. The number of modes actually adopted depends, of course, on the aircraft/control system combination; for example, in a single-engined light aircraft having a basic wing-levelling control system, only altitude and heading modes might comprise the outer loop control, whereas in a more complex type of transport aircraft using a flight guidance system, and having automatic landing capability, the outer loop could comprise all the modes listed in the table.

Manometric or air data

Raw data inputs which come under this heading are those associated with altitude, airspeed, vertical speed, and speed in terms of Mach number, each providing outer loop control about the pitch axis of an aircraft. Sensing may be carried out either by independent sensor units, or by a central air data computer. The sensors operate on the same fundamental principles as the basic pitot-static flight instruments, the measuring elements being coupled to appropriate types of electrical pick-off elements in lieu of indicating pointer mechanisms.

Altitude hold

As we learned from chapter 4, any changes of aircraft attitude about its pitch axis while in straight and level flight, will be detected by the pitch attitude sensing element of the automatic control system, and the changes will be accordingly corrected. However, in the event that the changes are associated with a pure vertical displacement of the aircraft, detection and corrections might still be effected, but straight and level flight could possibly be resumed at some altitude above or below that at which flight is required. In other words, an attitude sensing element alone cannot detect an altitude change, and neither can it maintain a required altitude. In order to meet this requirement, and also to provide for automatic 'levelling off' at any desired altitude, an altitude hold, or lock sensor, is employed. Sensors vary in construction, particularly in connection with the type of pick-off element adopted for a specific flight control system. The fundamentals of the operating requirement may, however, be understood by considering the example illustrated in fig. 6.2.

The sensor consists of a pressure transducer comprising an evacuated capsule assembly, an E and I type of inductive pick-off element (see page 103) an amplifier, and a two-phase induction type of chaser motor. The capsule assembly is subjected to changes of static pressure supplied to the case of the sensor unit from the aircraft's static pressure system, and is mechanically linked to the I bar of the pick-off element. A change of altitude produces a change of static pressure to cause the capsule assembly to expand or close up; this, in turn, displaces the I bar and a signal is induced in the coil of the centre limb of the E bar, the signal being a measure of the direction and rate of altitude change.

With the altitude hold mode unselected, the induced signal is fed to the chaser motor which drives the E bar in the same direction as the I bar, and so reduces the signal to zero. When the mode is selected, the pick-off will be in the zero signal condition at the prevailing altitude of the aircraft; this condition thus becomes the datum from which altitude changes may be detected. When a change does occur, the capsule assembly displaces the I bar which induces a proportional signal in the centre limb coil winding, the signal being analagous to an altitude error. The signal, which cannot now cause operation of the chaser motor, is applied to a separate error amplifier, and finally to the pitch channel servo amplifier. The elevator servomotor is thus operated to apply

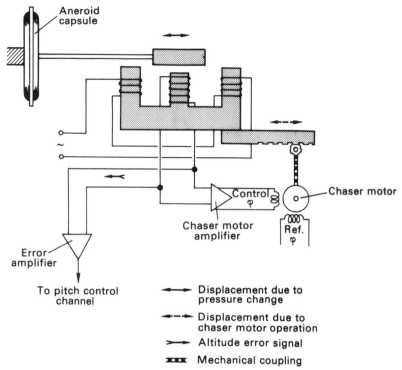

Aneroid capsule

Control φ — Chaser motor

Chaser motor amplifier

Ref. φ

Error amplifier

To pitch control channel

→ Displacement due to pressure change

←--→ Displacement due to chaser motor operation

>→ Altitude error signal

▪▪▪ Mechanical coupling

Fig. 6.2 Altitude-hold sensor

elevator control and so restore the aircraft to the selected altitude. At the same time, the change in static pressure will cause the capsule assembly to displace the I bar in the opposite direction to reduce the error signal to zero once again.

Another example of an altitude hold sensor which forms part of a central air data computer, is shown in fig. 6.3. In this case, the pressure transducer is connected to the cores in such a manner that they move differentially within the windings of a differential transformer element, to provide an altitude error signal from a zero signal condition. The signal is amplified and drives a chaser motor which, in turn, drives the transducer capsule assembly in a direction opposite to that caused by an altitude change, so reducing the error signal to zero. The chaser motor is also connected to two solenoid-operated clutches, one engaging ganged potentiometers, and the other a CX synchro rotor. The potentiometers are in the signal line to the pitch servomotor, their function being to attenuate control signals as a function of sensed static pressure, and thereby adjust control loop gains for optimum operation. The function of the CX synchro is to transmit the altitude error signal to the pitch servomotor which will operate to return the aircraft to the altitude it is required to hold.

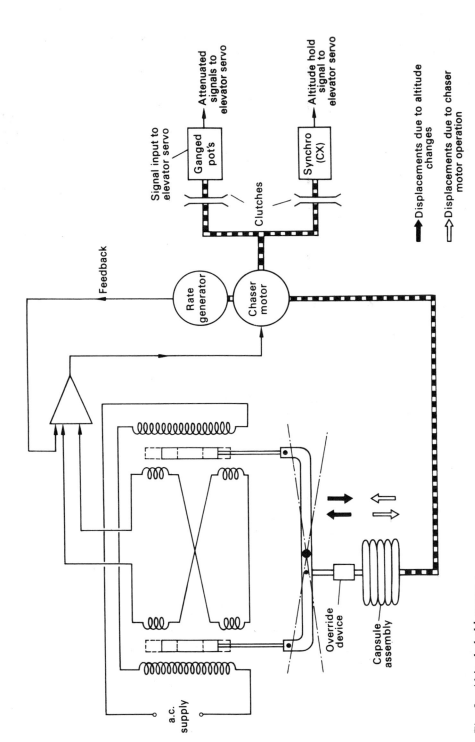

Fig. 6.3 Altitude-hold sensor

Another feature of this sensor is chaser motor damping to prevent oscillations as the motor and pick-off attain the zero signal position. This is accomplished by feeding back an opposing signal from a rate generator driven by the chaser motor. The linkage between the capsule assembly and the pick-off element contains a spring-loaded override device that opens the linkage when a pressure change is applied. This action also occurs if there is a pressure change on the capsule assembly when the electrical power is off, or when the altitude rate of change exceeds the dynamic range of the sensor. The linkage closes and the sensor becomes operative immediately the override conditions cease.

A unique type of altitude-hold sensor adopted in an autopilot designed for use in small aircraft is shown in fig. 6.4. In this case, the aneroid

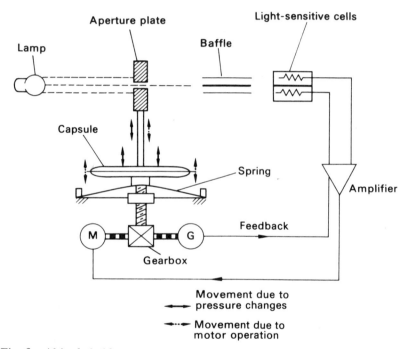

Fig. 6.4 Altitude-hold sensor

capsule actuates a detecting element, consisting of an aperture plate mounted on the capsule, an incandescent lamp, and two light-sensitive cells connected in a resistance bridge circuit. At a constant altitude, the aperture is centred with respect to the lamp, and the cells respond to equal amounts of light so that the bridge is in balance.

When the capsule expands or contracts as a result of an altitude change, the aperture plate is displaced, thereby deflecting the light beam from one or other of the cells causing an unbalanced condition in the bridge circuit. The resultant altitude error signal is amplified and is fed to the motor of a tachogenerator which then drives the complete assembly so as to centralise the aperture and thereby rebalance the bridge circuit. Overshoot of the balanced condition is prevented by a feedback signal from the generator which runs at a speed proportional to that of the motor. Thus, the sensor is continuously maintained in the balanced condition to provide the necessary flight level datum from which the altitude hold mode may be selected. This action is continuous until the hold mode is selected, at which point the altitude error signal voltage is switched from the tachogenerator motor to a summing network in the pitch control amplifier.

Any deviations from a selected altitude will result, therefore, in a signal being applied to the pitch servomotor to return the aircraft to that altitude. Under these conditions, cancelling of the altitude error signal and rebalancing of the bridge circuit is effected solely by the expansion or contraction of the capsule about the datum altitude.

Airspeed hold

Since airspeed-hold sensors are used in conjunction with altitude-hold sensors, in any one system design the methods of transmitting error signals are of a common nature; in fact, the only difference is that whereas an altitude sensor measures only static pressure changes, an airspeed sensor is required to measure the difference between static and dynamic pressures. The capsule assembly, instead of being sealed, is open to the source of dynamic pressure, and static pressure is admitted to the sealed chamber in which the assembly is contained. Thus, the capsule assembly expands or closes up under the influence of a pressure differential created by a change of airspeed. The pick-off element actuated by the capsule assembly, is identical in construction, and operation, to that adopted in the altitude sensor, the speed error signal also being supplied to the pitch servo control channel.

The airspeed-hold sensor associated with the altitude-hold sensor shown in fig. 6.3 utilises an identical type of pick-off element, but instead of the error signal being transmitted to the pitch control channel by a CX synchro, transmission is by means of ganged potentiometers driven by the chaser motor. The capsule assembly is housed in the same chamber as the altitude capsule assembly.

Mach hold

In high-performance aircraft, the airspeed is measured in terms of Mach number, in addition to the conventional unit of speed, knots. There is, therefore, a requirement for both modes under automatically controlled flight conditions, the airspeed hold mode being most commonly used during the low-altitude cruise phase of flight, and Mach hold during the high-altitude phase. Since Mach number varies with airspeed and altitude, the signal outputs from the independent sensors can be integrated to provide the required Mach signal output. This is accomplished by incorporating all sensors in a unit called a central air data computer.

Central air data computers

It is clear from the foregoing that the transmission of the raw data associated with airspeed, altitude, and Mach number is, primarily, the transmission of pressure from two sources; a static source and a dynamic source. In some types of aircraft, both sensors are combined in a pitot-static tube, or pressure head, which is located in the airflow at an experimentally determined point. In the large majority of aircraft, however, the sources are independent; dynamic pressure is detected by a pitot pressure tube in the airflow, while static pressure is detected by a vent located at a point of undisturbed airflow, for example, at the side of a fuselage.

The pressures are transmitted to the primary flight instruments, i.e. airspeed indicator, altimeter, and vertical speed indicator, via pipelines the length and quantity of which will vary according to the size of aircraft, and the number of stations within an aircraft at which indications of the relevant parameters are required. In order, therefore, to minimise the 'pressure plumbing' arrangements, the idea of supplying the pressures to a central location from which they could be transmitted to any number of stations, and in the form of synchronous signal data links, was developed and resulted in the design of units designated as central air data computers (CADC).

In common with other units and systems, a CADC can vary in design depending on a particular manufacturer's approach to the application of the fundamental principles involved; it is, therefore, beyond the scope of this book to go into specific operating details of the various computers in current use. However, the principal features of CADC design concept may be understood from fig. 6.5, which may be considered generally representative.

The computer is basically of the electro-mechanical analogue type, consisting of two pressure transducers, one for the measurement of airspeed and the other for measuring altitude. Each transducer is coupled to an inductive pick-off element the signals from which operate motors, gear trains and shafts; the rotation of the shafts being proportional to dynamic pressure and static pressure. As is the case with any airspeed and altitude indicating system, it is also necessary to

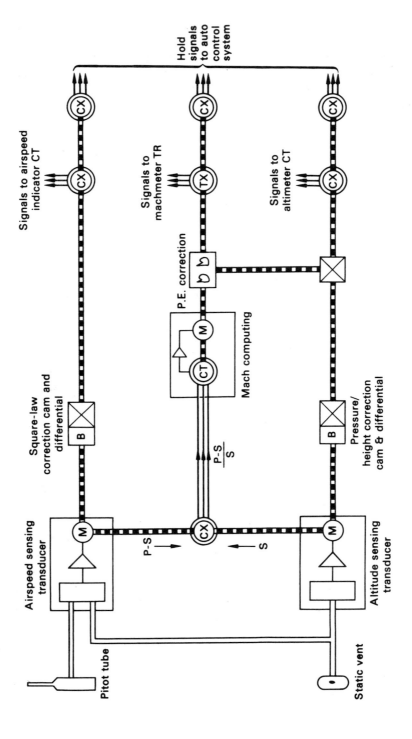

Fig. 6.5 Schematic arrangement of a central air data computer

correct the dynamic and the static pressure inputs to a CADC, for non-linear characteristics, i.e. the airspeed square-law, and the inverse pressure/altitude characteristic. Furthermore, corrections for errors arising from variations in airflow, which might possibly arise at a static vent location, must also be considered.

Corrections are accomplished by coupling accurately profiled cams to the appropriate output shafts driven by the motors of the pressure transducer pick-off elements. The cams are provided with 'followers' which actuate gear trains, and further output shafts coupled to the rotors of CX synchros, the stators of which are connected to CT synchros in an airspeed indicator, an altimeter, and in the relevant hold mode circuits of the automatic flight control system. Thus, the rotation of the shafts and the synchro signals are converted into the required linear outputs.

For the derivation of Mach number outputs, a somewhat different mechanical and synchronous data link arrangement is required because, as noted earlier, Mach number varies with airspeed and altitude. In terms of dynamic and static pressures, Mach number is equivalent to the ratio $(P-S)/S$; it is therefore necessary to convert the mechanical outputs from both the airspeed and altitude pressure transducers into an electrical signal corresponding to this ratio. In the example of CADC considered, this is effected by coupling the transducer output shafts, via cams, to a CX synchro, the dynamic output shaft being coupled to the stator, while the static output shaft is coupled to the rotor. The synchro therefore serves as a dividing mechanism to produce an angular output corresponding to the foregoing ratio.

The output is transmitted to the stator of a synchro control transformer (CT) contained within the Mach computing section which has no mechanical link with other sections of the computer. The output from the CT is then fed to an amplifier which energises the control phase of a servomotor causing it to drive the CT rotor to a position where it nulls the pressure ratio signal from the divider synchro CX. The motor also drives two cams, one to modify the motor output to ensure that the CT rotor is positioned in accordance with the required pressure ratio, and the second to correct the Mach number output for pressure error. The corrected output signal is fed to a torque synchro receiver TR contained within the Machmeter, and forming a synchronous data link with a TX, the rotor of which is positioned by the Mach computing section output shaft. Mach-hold mode signals are provided by a CX having its rotor coupled to the same shaft as that of the TX.

In any type of aircraft there are difficulties in measuring true static pressure because of variations in the pattern of the airflow at the location of the pitot-static pressure head, or the static vent. The airflow pattern varies according to the position of the pressure head, static vent, Mach number and altitude; under certain conditions, therefore, inaccuracies could be present. For conventional pitot-static flight instruments correction data are given in tabular or graphical form, the appropriate values being applied directly to indicated readings. In the case of a CADC, however, corrections are continuously and automatically applied, usually by means of cams profiled from values calculated to suit the conditions of a particular aircraft. The correction is applied as a function of Mach number, to the altitude and Mach number computing sections, the cams being connected to differential gear assemblies located between the pressure transducer and CX synchro of the altitude section, and between the CT and TX synchros of the Mach number section. Thus, the cams apply the pressure corrections, by modifying the angular positions of the output shafts, and the CX and TX synchro rotors, and consequently the output signals from the stators of these synchros.

Heading hold

As the name suggests, in this mode of operation the automatic flight control system holds the aircraft on a pre-selected magnetic heading. Since turning of an aircraft is carried out by displacement of the ailerons, the heading hold mode relates to control about the roll axis, and heading error signals are applied to the roll control channel of the flight control system. The error signals may be derived in a variety of ways depending on the source of magnetic heading data provided in a particular type of aircraft, and on how such source may be utilised in automatic flight control system operation.

In the case of some types of basic control systems utilising a directional gyro for the supplyhe of ading data within the turn control loop, it is usual to provide a heading selector which may be a separate unit or incorporated in the pilot's control panel (see fig. 6.6). In this example, the selector contains a heading dial which can be rotated by means of a setting knob so that it may be referenced to any heading indicated by the directional gyro. The dial is mechanically coupled to a CT synchro which develops a heading error signal voltage as a function of dial position. The heading set knob is also linked to a switch, and when the knob is pushed in the switch connects the error signal voltage to a summing amplifier in the roll control channel of the autopilot. Thus, the aircraft will turn on to the selected heading, and when this is reached the error signal is 'nulled' and the aircraft is held on the selected heading.

In the majority of aircraft, it is usual for heading data to be supplied

Heading selector

Fig. 6.6 Heading selector

from either a basic form of remote-indicating compass system, or from a more sophisticated flight director system (see chapter 8), the latter being capable of such integration with all other possible modes of operation, that an overall system of flight guidance may be constituted in the full meaning of the term.

In both the foregoing systems, heading data are obtained by direct sensing of the earth's magnetic field as opposed to directional gyro indications which must always be referenced to those of a magnetic compass. Sensing is effected by a flux detector unit located at some remote point in the aircraft, e.g. a wing tip, the detector forming the transmitter (CX) of a synchronous control system (see also page 107). In this application, the complete detector turns with the aircraft so that a resultant field is produced which is aligned with the earth's magnetic field. The signals induced in the transmitter coils are fed to the stator of a slaving CT synchro, the function of which is to monitor the azimuth position of a directional gyroscope via a slaving amplifier and torque motor. The gyroscope may be contained within a panel-mounted indicator, but more generally it is designed as a separate and remotely-located master unit. The fundamental arrangement of such a system is illustrated in fig. 6.7.

On a constant heading, the synchro system is in the 'null' condition, the heading being indicated by a heading card referenced against a lubber mark. During a turn, the flux detector senses the changing heading, and the field in the slaving CT synchro will rotate and thereby induce a heading error voltage in the synchro rotor. The signal is then amplified by the slaving amplifier and fed to the torque motor which precesses the directional gyroscope in azimuth and, at the same time,

143

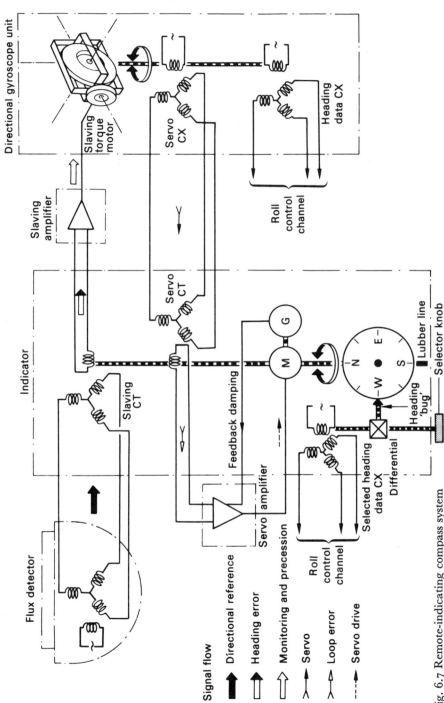

Fig. 6.7 Remote-indicating compass system

causes the rotor of a servo CX synchro to rotate. The signals induced in the stator of the CX are applied to that of a servo CT synchro in the indicator and, because turning of the aircraft causes mis-alignment to exist between the rotors of both synchros, a servo-loop error voltage is induced in the CT synchro rotor. This voltage is then applied to a servo amplifier and, after amplification, it is applied to the reference winding of a servomotor which is mechanically coupled to the CT synchro rotor and to the heading card of the indicator. Thus, the rotor and heading card are rotated, the card indicating the direction of the heading change taking place.

On cessation of the turn, the rotor reaches a 'null' position, and as there is no further input to the servo amplifier, the servomotor stops rotating. Oscillation of the servo system is prevented by velocity feedback damping signals from a tachogenerator which is also driven by the servomotor. The slaving CT synchro rotor is also coupled to the servomotor, the purpose of this being to drive the rotor in synchronism with the rotating field in the stator. Thus, during turns, the directional gyroscope is continuously slaved to the changes in magnetic heading, and by means of the servo synchro loop, the complete system is monitored such that when a turn ceases, the system is in a 'null' condition, and the indicator displays the corresponding heading.

In order to apply the foregoing principle of remote-heading indication to an automatic flight control system as a heading-hold mode of operation, and as a means of automatically turning an aircraft on to a selected heading, it is necessary to provide additional data synchros in the compass system. In the example shown in fig. 6.7, the data synchro for heading hold is contained within the directional gyroscope unit, its rotor position being controlled by the gyroscope in the same way as the servo CX synchro. The data synchro stator is connected to the roll control channel of the flight control system via the mode selector circuit; the stator output therefore, provides the heading hold reference.

The signals for turning the aircraft on to any desired heading are derived from a data CX synchro contained within the indicator. The synchro rotor is mechanically coupled to a selector knob via a differential gear which also drives a heading 'bug' with respect to the heading card. When the knob is rotated to select a heading, the synchro rotor induces an error signal proportional to the difference between the aircraft's heading and the selected heading, the signal being supplied to the roll control channel as a turn command. As the aircraft turns, the compass system will respond in the manner already described, until the aircraft is on the selected heading and the data synchro error signal is balanced out. The heading-hold mode is then selected so that the flight control system is monitored by the data CX synchro in the directional gyroscope unit.

Since the 'heading select' facility of the compass system provides automatic turn control it is comparable in function to the turn control provided on a pilot's control panel (see page 58). It is necessary, therefore, to incorporate an interlock circuit between the two to prevent their signals from opposing each other. Thus, before the heading selector knob is rotated, the turn control knob on the control panel must be at its centre 'detent' position. When the turn control knob is rotated from 'detent', the compass signal circuit to the roll control channel is interrupted, but because the compass system continuously senses the heading changes produced, the appropriate signals will be re-applied when the control knob is returned to 'detent'.

Turbulence penetration

Flight in turbulent air conditions can impose varying degrees of load on the structure of an aircraft, and although designed to withstand such loads, it is necessary for the pilot to adjust power and speed, and to operate the flight control system in a manner compatible with the flight conditions prevailing.

If an aircraft penetrates turbulent air conditions while under automatically-controlled flight, the control system will sense the turbulence as disturbances to aircraft attitude, but in applying corrective control it is possible for additional structural loads to be imposed. The reason for this is that the rate of control system response tends to get out of phase with the rate at which disturbances occur, with the result that control response tends to become 'stiffer'. In turbulent conditions, therefore, it is normal to disengage the automatic flight control system. In some current systems, however, turbulence penetration may be selected as a mode of operation such that the gain of both pitch and roll channels is reduced thereby 'softening' flight control system response to turbulence.

Instrument landing system

An Instrument Landing System (ILS) is a short-range navigational aid which provides azimuth and vertical guidance during the approach to an airport runway. The system comprises ground-based transmitting elements and also receiving elements carried on board an aircraft. The ground-based elements are: (i) a *localiser* which transmits runway azimuth approach information; (ii) a *glide path*, or glide slope, transmitter which provides vertical approach information; and (iii) *marker beacons* which transmit information on the distance to the runway threshold. The airborne elements are: (i) a *localiser signal receiving antenna* (usually this is the same antenna as the one used for the VOR installation since both the localiser element and the VOR operate in the same frequency band); (ii) a *glide path signal receiving antenna*; (iii) an *ILS receiver unit*; (iv) an *indicator* which shows whether the aircraft is on the correct approach path; (v) *marker beacon antenna and receiver*; and (vi) *marker lights* on the main instrument panel.

Localiser element

The transmitter is located at the far end of the runway and it transmits on a given frequency in the band 108.0 to 112.0 megahertz. To direct an approaching aircraft on to the extended centre line of the runway, the transmitter radiates azimuth guidance signals to the left and to the right of the centreline as shown in fig. 6.8. The signal transmitted to the left has a 90 Hz signal superimposed on it, while a 150 Hz signal is superimposed on the signal transmitted to the right. The two transmissions overlap along the runway centreline, and when an aircraft is approaching on the centreline extension, the ILS receiver receives both signals at equal strengths. This condition is indicated on the indicating element, usually by a vertical bar which takes up a central position over the dial of the indicating element.

If the aircraft deviates to the left of the centreline, the strength of the 90 Hz signal will be greater than that of the 150 Hz signal. Both signals pass through a comparator circuit within the receiver which then produces an output causing the vertical bar of the indicating element to be deflected to the right, thereby directing the pilot to 'fly right' in order to intercept the centreline again. Similarly, if the aircraft deviates to the right of the centreline, the 150 Hz signal is stronger than the 90 Hz signal, and so after comparison, the receiver output causes the vertical bar to be deflected to the left to direct the pilot to 'fly left' in order to intercept the centreline.

Glide path element

The transmitter is located near the threshold of the runway and it transmits on a given frequency in the band 329.3 to 335.0 megahertz. The glide path transmitter radiates a signal pattern which is similar to that of the localiser but, as will be noted from fig. 6.8, the transmissions provide vertical guidance above and below a descent path established at an angle of between 2.5° and 3°.

When the aircraft approaches along this path both the 90 Hz and 150 Hz signals are received at the same strength, and this is indicated by a horizontal bar or, as is more usual in present-day flight director

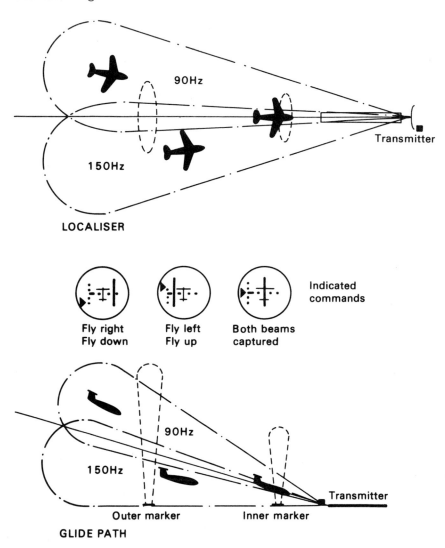

LOCALISER

Fly right
Fly down

Fly left
Fly up

Both beams
captured

Indicated
commands

Outer marker

Inner marker

GLIDE PATH

Fig. 6.8 ILS guidance signals and commands

systems, by a pointer which takes up a central position over a scale in the indicating element. If the aircraft deviates below or above the established path, the pointer will be deflected up or down and this will provide the pilot with the corresponding flight directions.

Indicating element

When ILS was first introduced, the deviations of an aircraft from the localiser and the glide path, were presented on a separate ILS indicator having a presentation as shown in fig. 6.9. However, with the introduction of integrated instrument systems, and flight director systems,

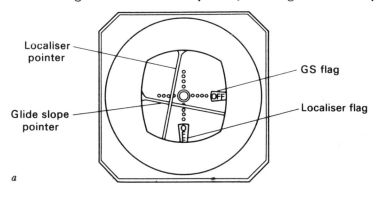

a

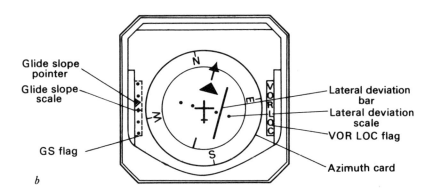

b

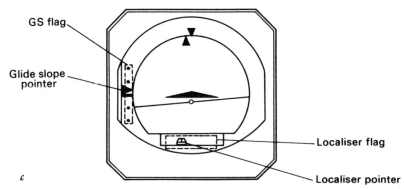

c

Fig. 6.9 ILS indicating elements   *a* ILS indicator   *b* Course deviation
c Attitude indicator

it was logical to combine the indications with the relevant instruments, and this is now current practice (see chapter 8). Although there are many types of these systems in use, each varying in the method of data presentation, the examples of the latter shown in fig. 6.9, may be considered generally representative of such methods. In all cases, the localiser bar, or lateral deviation bar as it is more usually referred to, and the glide path pointer are deflected by independent meter movements to which the respective receiver channel signals are supplied. Scales are provided for reference against the localiser bar and glide path pointer, and thereby indicate by a series of dots the amount of deviation in degrees from the respective beam centrelines. For example, a two-dot deflection of the localiser bar corresponds to an aircraft deviation of 2.5°, and a full-scale deflection of the glide path pointer corresponds to a deviation of 0.5°. The dots are also indicative of the value (in microamps) of the signal currents producing meter deflections. Warning flags are provided and are visible when power is off, whenever signals are below the required strength, and whenever any malfunction or failure of the system occurs.

Marker beacons

Marker beacon transmitters are located at points along the runway approach path (see fig. 6.8), and their signals are beamed vertically into the descent path on a frequency of 75 megahertz. The signals are coded, and when an aircraft flies over a beacon, they are received and can be heard over the aircraft's intercommunication system; they also illuminate appropriately coloured lights on the cockpit instrument panel. The outer marker is situated approximately four nautical miles from the runway threshold, and for identification purposes, its transmitted signals are coded with continuous dashes. The inner marker is sited approximately 3,500 feet from the threshold, its signals being coded with alternate dots and dashes.

ILS coupling

When an aircraft's navigation receiver has been tuned to a localiser frequency, the glide path frequency is also automatically tuned in, since for a given localiser frequency there is a corresponding glide path frequency. The receiver output signals are fed to the appropriate indicating element, and by following the displayed commands a pilot is able to carry out an ILS approach to an airport runway. Such an approach is normally effected in two stages; in the first stage, the aircraft intercepts and captures the localiser beam so that it is aligned with the extended centre line of the runway, while in the second stage, the aircraft intercepts and captures the glide path beam enabling it to fly in alignment with the runway and also in the correct pitch attitude.

In order to carry out the approach under automatic control it is necessary for the flight control system to be 'coupled' to the ILS so that the system will capture the beams smoothly and at the desired beam angles. The coupling is initiated by selecting the appropriate switches on the mode selector panel.

As we have already learned, ILS signals are purely of the command type and they vary in amplitude with displacement from beam centres but, since they have no directional properties, in the sense that they cannot take into account the heading of an aircraft with respect to the runway, coupling of these signals alone to an automatic flight control system would serve no useful purpose. For example, if a localiser signal provides a 'fly right' command, and the aircraft is on such a heading that it does not come within the normal width of the beam, then such a command would remain constant for the reason that the localiser signal at that part of the beam is a constant. If this signal were to be supplied to the control channel of an automatic control system, the aircraft could well be flown in a circle, and with little chance of capturing the beam. Similarly, if heading data alone were supplied to a control channel, the heading error signals would be proportional to the difference between actual heading of the aircraft and runway direction, and would provide a 'fly left' command resulting in the aircraft flying parallel to the localiser beam.

In the practical case, therefore, it is necessary to feed the signals from both sources to the roll control channel of an automatic control system, the beam intercept and tracking commands being the resultant of both signals. The effects are shown in fig. 6.10. At point 'A', it is assumed that the aircraft is under automatic control in the heading mode of operation, and that the ILS localiser frequency has been tuned in. The deviation pointer of the appropriate indicator will, therefore, display a 'fly left' command. In order to satisfy the command, the aircraft must, of course, change its heading and since it is being flown in the heading mode, the change can be made via the heading selector of the appropriate indicator. The heading selected is the magnetic direction, or QDM as it is called, of the runway. Thus, a heading error signal is established and is applied to the roll control channel which then initiates turning of the aircraft on to an intercept heading. The localiser (LOC) mode is then selected so that the roll control channel can now respond to the resultant of the beam signal and the heading error signal. When the heading is such that the signals are in balance, the aircraft is then controlled so that it will fly straight and level on the intercept heading (point 'B') and at an angle governed by the ratio between the beam and heading signals. By pre-adjustment of the signal circuits, the angle of intercept can be set at a constant value as required for a particular automatic flight control system; some typical values are 35°, 45° and 65°. As the aircraft enters the normal width of the beam (in which the signal is proportional to deviation) the signal is correspondingly reduced, and the now predominant QDM signal causes the aircraft to turn towards the centre of the beam until both beam and QDM signals are again in balance. This control action is continuous

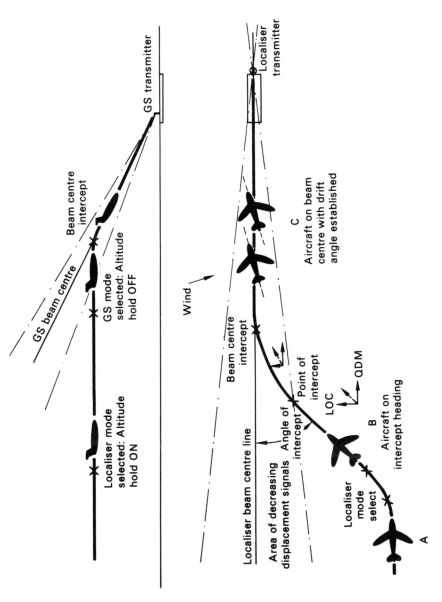

Fig. 6.10 ILS coupling

until the aircraft is on the beam centre line and tracking it, when both the beam and QDM signals are reduced to zero.

During an automatic approach, allowance must also be made for the effects of crosswinds, otherwise the aircraft would take up a position downwind of the localiser beam centre and would fly a 'stand-off' track parallel to the beam, and at a particular drift or 'crab' angle. The distance from the beam centre and the crab angle would depend on the strength of the crosswind, and because the aircraft takes up a position where the beam and QDM signals balance each other, 'stand-off' and crab angle would be maintained. The method of compensating for crosswind effects varies depending on the type of automatic control system. In some cases, it is necessary to pre-calculate the drift angle appropriate to the wind conditions, and to adjust the compass indicator such that its indications and heading error signal output are offset from the QDM by the amount of drift angle. The relevant signal circuits are so arranged that the aircraft is turned in response to the localiser beam signal, and when this and the heading error signal are reduced to zero, the aircraft is then flown along the beam centre line with its heading off-set by the drift angle (point 'C' in fig. 6.10).

In a number of systems, it is more usual to supply part of the beam signal to an integrator circuit with a long time-constant (see also page 128). The circuit is activated when the aircraft is near the beam centre line, i.e. when the beam signal falls to a low value, and remains in action until the signal has fallen to zero. Since the presence of a crosswind slows the speed of interception of the beam centre line, the integrator signal is built up in proportion to the amount of crosswind. The build up continues until the beam centre line is reached, at which point the aircraft's heading is controlled by the integrator signal and the pre-selected heading signal.

As noted earlier, when the navigation receiver is tuned to the localiser frequency, the glide path frequency is also tuned in; thus, when the aircraft is correctly established on the localiser beam, the glide path signals can be used to effect the final phase of the approach. The glide path can be intercepted and captured while the aircraft is being flown in the altitude-hold mode, and from above or below the glide path. Ultimately, the aircraft must, therefore, fly through the glide path and its proximity will be evidenced by 'fly down' or 'fly up' commands of the associated indicator. At the point of beam interception, the glide path mode is selected on the mode selector panel, and the beam signals are then supplied to the pitch control channel of the flight control system. Thereafter, changes of position of the aircraft from the glide path produces control channel response to restore the required pitch attitude.

At the same time that the glide-path mode is selected, the altitude-hold mode is automatically disconnected. A pitch control channel incorporates a circuit network which phase advances the glide path error signals so that they are damped to give progressively tighter control as the aircraft flies down the glide path, and thereby allowing for the converging nature of the beam. In flight control systems which use a vertical gyroscope as the attitude sensing element, the pitch error signal produced would tend to 'back off' the beam error signal and cause the aircraft to fly above the beam. This is prevented by passing the signals through an integrator circuit.

VOR system

A VOR (VHF omni-directional radio range) system not unlike the ILS is a short-range navigational aid comprising ground-based transmitting stations, or beacons, and receiving elements carried on board an aircraft. It differs in function however, in that it provides en-route information on the bearing of an aircraft from the points at which the stations are geographically located. The stations are spaced at intervals of 50 to 80 nautical miles within what is termed the 'airways system'.

A VOR station transmits a very high frequency (VHF) carrier wave operating in the 108 to 118 MHz band, and on which are superimposed two low frequency modulating signals. One of these signals, known as the reference signal, is radiated in all directions (hence the term omni-directional) with a fixed phase, while the other is a rotating beam signal and varies in phase to produce an infinite number of 'radials'. Thus, at any particular point relative to the station (which is lined up on magnetic north) a specific phase relationship exists between the two signals, and this is indicated in fig. 6.11. Each station is identified by a Morse code signal which is received by the navigation receiver in the aircraft when the corresponding station transmitting frequency has been selected. The display of bearing information is presented on an indicator mounted on the aircraft's main instrument panel. The type of indicator depends on the equipment specified for a particular type of aircraft; for example, it may be an omni-bearing indicator, a radio magnetic indicator, or it may be a horizontal situation display indicator which forms part of a flight director system (see chapter 8). In general, however, the display is comprised of three main indicating elements: (i) a bearing scale or an index, which is positioned by a selector knob to indicate the radial on which the aircraft is to be flown; (ii) a deviation pointer indicating whether the aircraft is flying on the radial; and (iii) a TO-FROM indicator to indicate whether the aircraft is flying towards a station or away from it. A warning flag is also provided to

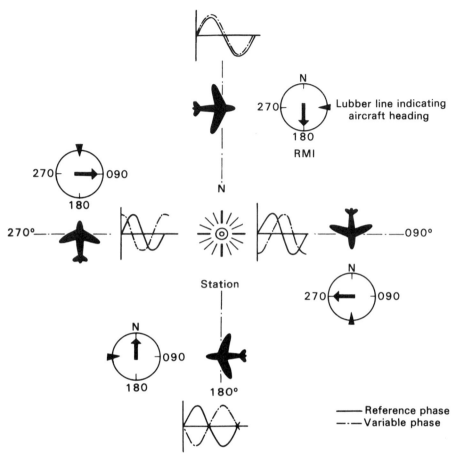

Fig. 6.11 VOR system

indicate 'system off', receiving of low-strength signals, or no signals at all.

Fig. 6.12 illustrates an omni-bearing indicator, and this serves as a useful example in understanding the fundamentals of VOR operation as a navigational aid. After a station has been identified from its Morse signal and tuned-in, the omni-bearing selector knob is rotated to set the required bearing on the bearing scale, and also to position the rotor of a resolver synchro. The navigation receiver which continuously compares the phases of the transmitted signals, and compares them in turn with the phase shift produced in the resolver synchro, supplies an output signal to a meter movement controlling the vertical pointer of the indicator. When the pointer lies in the centre of the indicator it indicates that the phasing of the required bearing radial signals has been matched and that further rotation of the selector knob is unnecessary. The reading shown on the bearing scale at that instant

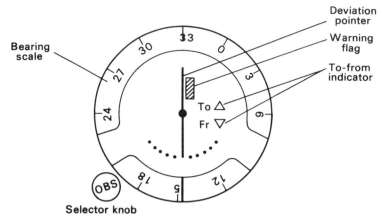

Fig. 6.12 Omni-bearing indicator

indicates the heading on to which the aircraft must be turned in order to fly along the corresponding radial to the station.

At the same time, the TO-FROM indicator indicates TO usually by means of an arrow-shaped pointer. Any departure from the radial as a result of, say, crosswind drift, the deviation pointer will be deflected to one or other side, and so command a turn in the direction of the deflection in order to intercept the radial once again. Thus, the command function is identical to that of the localiser pointer of an ILS indicator and, since localiser and VOR operate in the same frequency band, omni-bearing indicators and the indicators of flight director systems, are in fact designed such that their deviation pointers serve the dual command function.

As the aircraft approaches overhead the station, so the deviation pointer mechanism becomes more sensitive as a result of the convergence of the radials, and its indications, together with those of the TO-FROM indicator, become erratic. In this part of the approach, overhead the station and in departing from it, the aircraft is said to be in the 'cone of confusion'. The extent of the cone varies with altitude and groundspeed, typically from a few seconds at low altitude, to as much as two minutes at high altitude. Outbound flight from the station is indicated by the TO-FROM indicator changing to FROM and, provided an accurate heading is maintained, the deviation pointer continues to give corrective command information for the interception of the outbound radial.

VOR coupling

Operation in the VOR coupled mode is similar in many respects to that of the localiser mode, in that it also involves the capture of radio signal beams radiated in azimuth in association with steering commands from magnetic heading data; such data, however, being related to a pre-selected VOR station radial instead of a runway QDM. When the navigation receiver has been tuned to the station frequency and the required radial has been selected on the course indicator, coupling to the roll control channel is initiated by selecting the LOC/VOR mode. As a result of the convergence of the radials, and of the cone of confusion over a VOR station, the signal from a selected radial is unreliable and could, therefore, cause the automatic flight control system to carry out unwanted manoeuvres. To prevent this, it is usual to 'cut off' the VOR signal at the entrance to the cone of confusion, so that the roll control channel responds only to heading data signals. Cut off takes place automatically and is maintained for a pre-set time period, after which, and with the aircraft departing from the cone of confusion, the VOR signal corresponding to the outbound radial is switched in.

Inertial navigation system

The requirement for the navigation of an aircraft is, quite simply, the one of determining its position in relation to its point of departure, and points en-route, in order to reach a known destination. The basic data necessary for this purpose are principally time, speed, distance between points, longitude and latitude, magnetic heading, wind speed and direction, and bearings relative to known points on the earth's surface and to celestial points. The provision of such data is made by a variety of navigational aids, most of which are dependent on an external reference of one form or another.

Although such aids can provide reasonably accurate answers to the problems associated with the navigational task, the remaining errors involved make them only relatively useful. In the continuing development of navigational aids, particularly in relation to the stringent requirements laid down for the strategic roles of military aircraft, for missiles, and for spacecraft, it became essential to provide aids having much greater accuracy. These also needed to be independent of references derived from ground-based navigational beacons in particular. The attendant research ultimately resulted in the application of a theory which, as is so often the case, is based on old established laws; in this instance the theory of inertia applied to what subsequently became known as an Inertial Navigation System (INS), the basic elements of which are shown schematically in fig. 6.13. The navigational problems which can be solved by INS are shown in fig. 6.14.

Inertial theory is based on Newton's second law, i.e. that force is

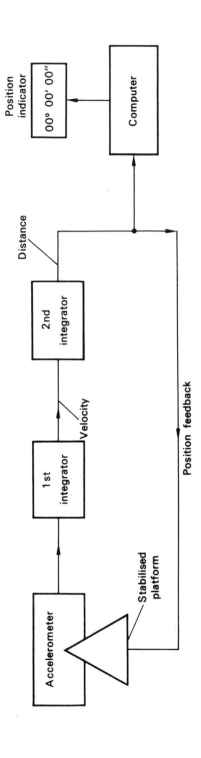

Fig. 6.13 Basic elements of an inertial navigation system

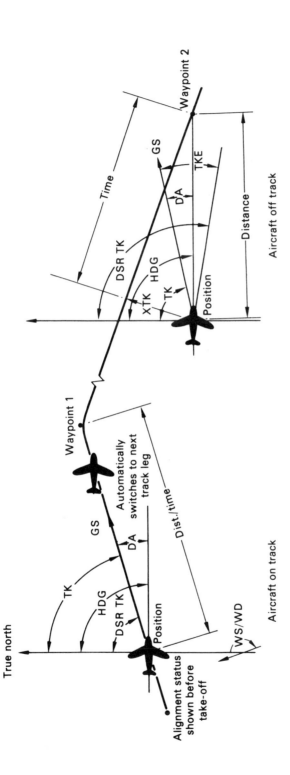

Fig. 6.14 Navigational problems solved by INS

GS (*Ground speed*): Speed of aircraft over surface of earth.
DA (*Drift angle*): Angle in degrees that aircraft track is to right or left of aircraft heading.
TKE (*Track angle error*): Angle in degrees that aircraft track is to left or right of desired track.
XTK (*Cross track*): Distance left or right from desired track to present position, measured perpendicular to track desired.

TK (*Track*): Actual path of aircraft over earth's surface. Measured clockwise from true north through 360°.
DSR TK (*Desired track*): A great circle path on surface of earth connecting two waypoints.
HDG (*Heading*): Angle between true north and longitudinal axis of aircraft.

equal to time rate of change of momentum, without approximation or correction for any effect. In plainer terms, it can be stated that velocity is the rate of change of distance with time, and acceleration is the rate of change of velocity with time. If this deduction is reversed, it can be seen that a vehicle's position at any time after starting to move can be determined solely from its acceleration history, and by double integration of measured accelerations the distance travelled during a given time may also be determined.

A typical INS comprises the three principal units illustrated in fig. 6.15; they are a mode selector unit, an inertial navigation unit comprising a digital computer and inertial platform, and a control display unit. The 'core' of the system is the inertial platform which establishes the stable reference plane from which measurements can be computed. The inputs needed to keep the system in touch with the outside world come from accelerometer-actuated pick-off elements, the signals being fed to the computer in proportion to acceleration forces. Since the functions of navigational geometry lie in a horizontal plane, two accelerometers are mounted on the platform; one oriented north-south, the other oriented east-west. Thus, the computer is able to record the acceleration history of an aircraft, and therefore determine its position in relation to its starting point. Angles that fall between the north-south or east-west relationship are calculated by the computer solving algebraic vector problems. A third accelerometer measures acceleration in the vertical direction.

To make the measurements refer only to translational accelerations, the accelerometers must at all times be maintained in accurate alignment with their respective directions, i.e. the platform must be maintained in correct azimuth alignment. This is accomplished by mounting the platform in a gimbal ring system and controlling the position of the rings by three rate-integrating gyroscopes and servomotors. In addition, the platform must be maintained accurately horizontal in relation to the earth's surface in order to prevent the accelerometers from sensing misleading gravity accelerations. Errors resulting from earth rate and transport rate (see pages 69 and 71) and from Coriolis effect, are also automatically corrected by computed signals applied to the servomotors.

The arrangement of the inertial platform is schematically shown in fig. 6.16. The gyroscopes actuate pick-off elements, the signals from which are supplied to the servomotors via the computer, so that any displacement of the platform axis will cause one of the gyroscopes to precess and the resultant pick-off signal causing a servomotor to rotate that axis of the platform back to its original alignment in space. To allow for the particular relationship of the stable element to the outer gimbal ring, the servomotor signals pass through a resolver synchro.

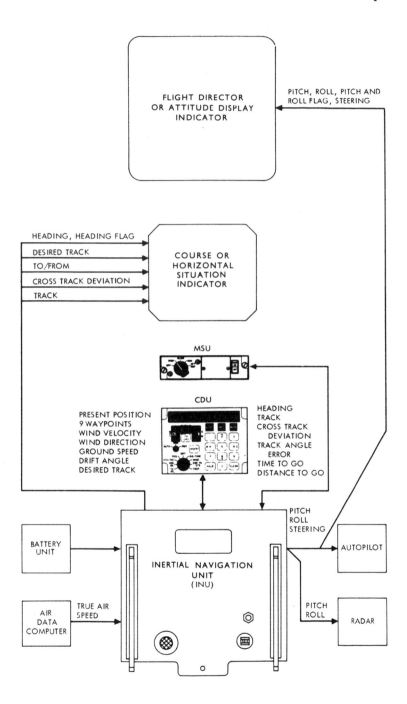

Fig. 6.15 Inertial navigation system units

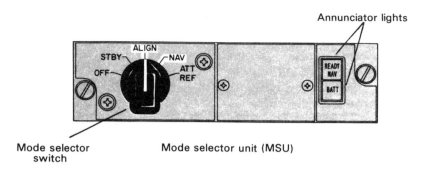

Mode selector
switch

Mode selector unit (MSU)

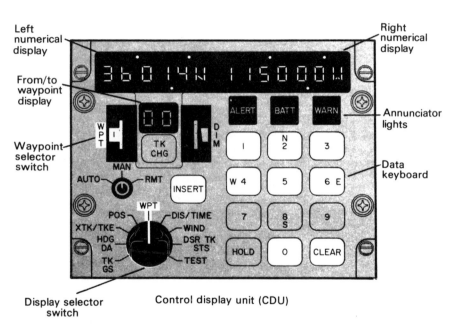

Display selector
switch

Control display unit (CDU)

Fig. 6.15 Inertial navigation system units (*contd.*)

To allow for change in latitude, the output of the north-south accelerometer is doubly integrated so that the angular acceleration of the aircraft above the earth's centre can be followed. A slightly more complex correction must be applied to allow for changes in longitude because such changes are also dependent upon latitude. The output velocity signal of the east-west accelerometer integrator is therefore multiplied by the secant of the latitude and then passed to the platform monitoring servomotor.

The inertial platform has one further characteristic and that is of being tuned so that at all times it accurately seeks a local vertical

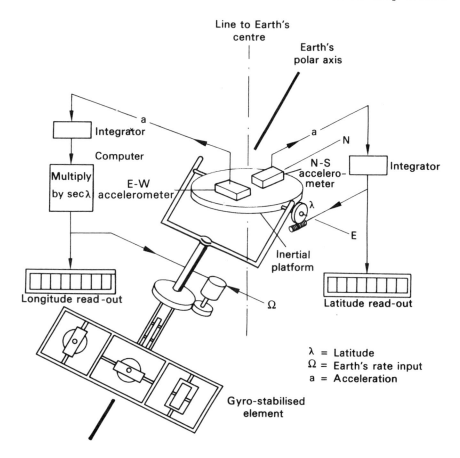

Fig. 6.16 Schematic arrangement of inertial platform

reference coincident with the earth's centre. This is achieved by applying the principle of what is known as the Schuler pendulum in such a way that by utilising error compensations from the computer together with a mathematical model in the computer, the platform is made to behave like a pendulum whose arm is equal in length to the earth's radius, and whose centre of rotation is coincident with the earth's centre. The result is that any build-up of errors in the accelerometers and gyroscopes is limited and minimised, and the platform stays parallel to the earth's surface regardless of which latitude and longitude it is put into operation.

The digital computer continuously solves the associated navigation equations, from the signal data fed into it by the control display unit, and by a central air data computer. The signals from the latter relate to true airspeed, which information is used for determining wind speed and direction and thereby the drift angle, and to altitude information for damping an integrating loop in altitude computation. Output signals are used for displaying computed data, and also for manoeuvring the aircraft towards the selected waypoint, via the roll channel of the automatic flight control system.

The control display unit utilises a digital readout which presents the pilot with all the data necessary for monitoring flight progress. Information for display is inserted or requested by means of a 'keyboard'; it can also be obtained by turning the knob of a data selector switch to desired settings. A digital readout also provides information on the changes of track of the aircraft as it proceeds from one waypoint to the next.

Prior to departure, and before any movement of the aircraft takes place, the system is operated in a 'standby' and an 'align' mode, during which the inertial platform is automatically aligned to the aircraft's axes. The latitude and longitude of the aircraft at its departure position are also inserted at the control display unit, and this information is integrated into a mathematical model within the computer and, by a procedure known as gyrocompassing, the system is also aligned to its north reference point. The co-ordinates of the en route waypoints and of the destination are also subsequently entered in the control display unit. When the alignment sequence is completed, an annunciator light illuminates to indicate that the system is 'ready to navigate' and that following selection of the navigate mode on the mode selector unit, the aircraft may commence its flight.

During flight, and approximately two minutes before a waypoint is reached, a light on the control panel comes on, and then begins to flash on and off thirty seconds before the waypoint is crossed, thereby signalling for the aircraft to be turned. With the automatic flight control system engaged, the INS supplies command signals to the roll control channel so that the aircraft will automatically roll into a turn towards the waypoint and will level out on the new heading from the waypoint. This is repeated at each en-route waypoint until the final destination is reached.

Control wheel steering

A control wheel steering mode (CWS) is provided in some automatic flight control systems, its purpose being to enable the pilot to manoeuvre his aircraft in pitch or roll, through the automatic control system by exerting normal manoeuvring forces on the control wheel. When the control wheel is released, the automatic control system holds the aircraft at the newly-established attitude. The pitch and roll forces applied by the pilot are sensed by force transducers mounted in the hub of the control wheel, and they generate output voltage signals proportional to the forces; the signals are supplied to the pitch and roll channels of the automatic flight control system.

In some cases, limits may be imposed, e.g. if a roll angle is less than $5°$, wing levelling will automatically occur, and the control system will hold the aircraft on a heading established one second after the wings are level. Prior to, and during, capture phases of radio navigation modes of operation, the pilot can use CWS for supervisory override of the automatic flight control system. Thus, with the aid of the CWS mode, the pilot always has a control capability of the aircraft, and the aircraft does not have to follow a pre-programmed flight path when particular conditions dictate a different manoeuvre.

7
Conversion of Command Signals to Powered Control

The power output element of any automatic flight control system consists of servomotors, or servo-actuators as they are sometimes called, connected into the aircraft's primary flight control system circuits; the number of servomotors employed is governed by the number of control loops required. In addition to the actuation of primary flight controls, servomotors may also be used, in some cases, for the actuation of the secondary flight controls provided for trimming purposes and for yaw damping (see pages 173 and 177).

In general, servomotors operate on either electro-pneumatic, electro-mechanical, or electro-hydraulic principles, the choice, and constructional features adopted in applying such principles being dependent on the type of automatic control system, and on the methods adopted for actuation of the primary flight control surfaces. Servomotors may be connected either in series or in parallel with the normal flight control system of an aircraft. A series-connected servomotor is one which moves the flight control surfaces without moving the pilot's controls, while a parallel-connected servomotor moves both the control surfaces and the pilot's controls.

Electro-pneumatic servomotor

An example of a servomotor designed for use in one particular type of three-axis autopilot system is shown schematically in fig. 7.1. It consists of an electro-magnetic valve assembly, comprised of dual poppet valves which are connected via pressure ports and orifices to two cylinders containing pistons sealed against pressure loss by rolling diaphragms (also called 'roll-frams'). The valves are controlled by electrical command signals from the autopilot signal processing element, and the pressure for actuation of the pistons is supplied either from an

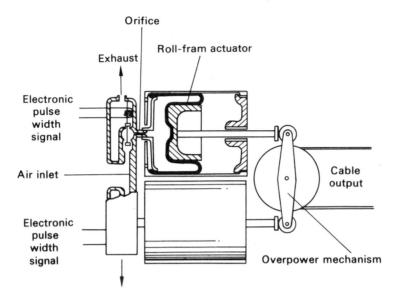

Fig. 7.1 Electro-pneumatic servomotor

engine-driven pump or from a tapping at a turbine engine compressor stage. The operating pressure is determined by the control force characteristics of the aircraft in which the particular autopilot is installed; a typical pressure range is from 7.5 to 30 lb/in². The piston rods are designed to drive an output linkage assembly which is connected to the appropriate flight control system circuit through a cable drum. The control input to the solenoid of each poppet valve is, in this example, a 22 Hz pulse-width modulated, square-wave signal, the particular frequency being chosen for minimum pressure disturbance and maximum valve life. The input pulses alternately open and close the valves.

With no command input, each valve is open for an equal period of time, and so there is equal pressure in both cylinders and no output torque is transmitted to the control system. When a control command signal is introduced, the open-time period of one valve is increased, while the open-time of the other valve is decreased. Thus, a differential pressure is developed in the two cylinders causing one piston rod to be extended and the other to be retracted, thereby causing rotation of the output linkage and deflection of the control surface(s) to which it is connected. A fixed orifice is installed at the inlet to each cylinder, the size of the orifice being selected to establish the response rate, or control gain, for the particular aircraft type.

As is conventional for the power output element of any automatic control system, the output linkage assembly of the servomotor shown can operate in any of three conditions: namely dis-engaged, engaged, and override. In the dis-engaged condition, the links and piston rods are retracted, allowing free rotation of the output shaft and cable drum, which is connected into the control system, to equal or to exceed the stop-to-stop travel of the appropriate control surface. When the servo-motor is pressurised on engagement of the autopilot, the piston rods and links move into contact with the output shaft arm and limit rotation of the arm such that the nominal control range of the autopilot does not exceed 50 % of the range of the aircraft's flight control system. To provide full control capability for overriding the automatic control system, the linkage assembly is articulated, but is normally held rigid by springs. Application of override force by the pilot allows deflection of the springs, and provides extension of the servomotor's nominal control range to that of the flight control system.

Electro-mechanical servomotors

Depending on the type of automatic control system, these servomotors may utilise either direct current or alternating current for operation. An example of a direct current operated servomotor is shown in fig. 7.2.

Fig. 7.2 Direct current-operated servomotor

It consists of a motor which is coupled to the flight control system via an electro-magnetic clutch, a gear train, and a sprocket and chain. The servomotor also carries a transistorised servo amplifier which amplifies the error signal transmitted by the attitude sensing element pick-off. Feedback is provided by a potentiometer, the wiper of which is driven by the motor.

Alternating current-operated servomotors may be either of the two-phase induction motor type, or of the type using the principle of hysteresis as applied to the gyroscopes of certain attitude sensing elements (see page 80). The two-phase induction motor type of servo-motor (fig. 7.3) has its reference phase constantly supplied with

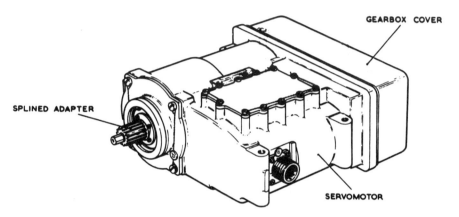

Fig. 7.3 Two-phase induction type servomotor

115 volts alternating current at a frequency of 400 Hz. The control phase is supplied by the output of the associated servo amplifier, the voltage varying from zero to 240 volts. The motor drives an output pulley via a gear train, and an electromagnetic clutch, the pulley providing the coupling between the servomotor and cable of the aircraft's flight control system. A CX synchro, and a device known as a rate generator, are also geared to the motor, their respective functions being to provide feedback, and to damp out any oscillations of the servo loop.

A servomotor utilising a hysteresis motor is shown in fig. 7.4. It operates on the same fundamental principle as the gyroscope motor described on page 80, but whereas in the latter the stator is directly connected to a three-phase supply of 115 volts at 400 Hz to produce a unidirectional rotating field, the three-phase stator in the example of servomotor illustrated, is fed from a single-phase supply, and field rotation in either direction is obtained by splitting the phases by means of capacitors. The single-phase supply is connected to, or disconnected

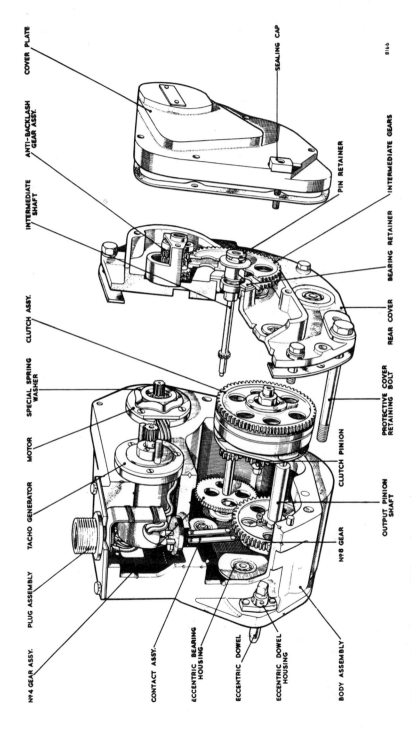

COVER PLATE

SEALING CAP

ANTI-BACKLASH GEAR ASSY.

PIN RETAINER

INTERMEDIATE GEARS

INTERMEDIATE SHAFT

BEARING RETAINER

CLUTCH ASSY.

REAR COVER

SPECIAL SPRING WASHER

PROTECTIVE COVER RETAINING BOLT

MOTOR

CLUTCH PINION

TACHO GENERATOR

OUTPUT PINION SHAFT

PLUG ASSEMBLY

Nº8 GEAR

Nº4 GEAR ASSY.

CONTACT ASSY.

ECCENTRIC BEARING HOUSING

ECCENTRIC DOWEL

ECCENTRIC DOWEL HOUSING

BODY ASSEMBLY

B166

Fig. 7.4 Servomotor utilising a hysteresis motor

from, the stator by means of switching devices known as silicon controlled rectifiers (SCRs). Activation, or 'firing', of one or other SCR is achieved by connecting the firing circuit to those circuits supplying the command signals which determine the direction in which the stator field, and hence the servomotor, must rotate in order to apply corrective control. Coupling between the motor and the aircraft's flight control system is by means of a gear train and an electromagnetic clutch, and feedback signals are supplied by a rate generator coupled to the motor gear train.

Servomotor mountings

Servomotors, as we have already noted, are mechanically connected into the cable runs of an aircraft's primary flight control system. The method of connection is governed by such factors as the type of automatic system, and the type of primary flight control system with which it is to be used. In those systems which may be considered as more basic in concept, servomotors are designed to have a direct method of connection, i.e. their output shafts are fitted with either a cable drum or sprocket around which control cable or chain may be directly fitted. In the application of a number of systems, however, there is another factor which has to be taken into consideration; this relates to the disturbing effect which the removal and replacement of servomotors, under certain aspects of system maintenance, might have on the settings and adjustments made to a primary flight control system. In order, therefore, to minimise this effect a large majority of systems utilise servomotors which are designed for attachment to, and removal from, special mountings connected into the primary control system on a more permanent basis.

Electro-hydraulic servo control

In primary flight control systems of the hydraulic power-operated type, displacements of the control surfaces are effected through the medium of servo control units; it is therefore possible to directly apply automatic control command signals to these units and thereby eliminate the need for independent servomotors, as in the conventional forms of automatic control systems. This control concept is adopted in several types of high-performance aircraft for elevator and rudder control, the latter serving the role of yaw damping in particular. In some aircraft, aileron control may also be effected through a hydraulic servo control unit, but where this is not the case a conventional type of servomotor is adopted.

An example of an elevator control system is schematically illustrated

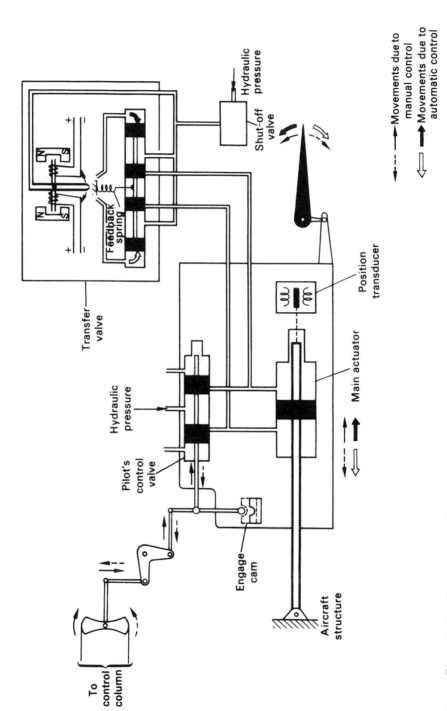

Fig. 7·5 Electro-hydraulic servo control

in fig. 7.5. The principal components of the control unit directly associated with automatic control are (i) shut-off valve, (ii) transfer valve, (iii) engage cam, and (iv) position transducer for supplying feedback signals.

During manual operation, and as the pilot moves the control column, the interconnecting cables cause rotation of the main quadrant, and since the engage cam is out of its detent, the input linkages of the control unit are free to rotate about their pivot points and so cause displacement of the pilot's control valve. Hydraulic fluid is thus transmitted to one or other side of the main actuator piston which, being secured to the aircraft structure, causes the fluid pressure to react on the unit housing so that it moves relative to the main actuator piston. The elevators are thus displaced in the required direction. Similar relative movement takes place at the pilot's control valve, and this serves as mechanical feedback to re-centre the valve as the control unit and the elevators reach their commanded positions.

When automatic control is selected, the engage signal is fed to the shut-off valve which then opens to admit hydraulic fluid to the transfer valve. At the same time, the engage cam locks the input linkages and prevents the pilot's control valve from moving with respect to the control unit housing. Automatic control command signals from the appropriate servo amplifier are also fed to the transfer valve which is of the electromagnetically-controlled type. As the signals are received, the valve is actuated so that it directs hydraulic fluid to one or other end of the main actuator; this, in turn, results in pressure reaction and elevator displacement, as in the case of manual operation. Since the pilot's control valve is locked to the control unit housing, it moves with it and causes the control cables and pilot's control column to follow; in other words, the system operates as a parallel type. As the control unit housing moves, it actuates the linear position transducer which provides the feedback signals necessary for limiting and taking off control as commands are satisfied.

Automatic trim control

In addition to the servo control of primary flight control surfaces, it is also necessary to provide methods of controlling the trim of an aircraft via its secondary flight control system (see also page 37). However, whereas in manually-controlled flight, trimming is usually effected about the three axes, under automatically controlled conditions it is generally confined to control about the pitch axis. In most cases it is accomplished by a separate trim servomotor coupled to the elevator trim tab system, and operating in parallel with the elevator servomotor.

An example of a trim tab servomotor is shown in fig. 7.6. For those aircraft in which trimming is effected by means of a variable incidence horizontal stabiliser, a separate trim servomotor may be coupled to the stabiliser; or in cases where the stabiliser incidence is varied by hydraulic motors (e.g. Boeing 747) the required automatic trim signals are used to control the flow of hydraulic fluid to the motors.

Sprocket for chain
drive to tab

Fig. 7.6 Trim tab servomotor

In certain types of small aircraft, the trim tab control system comprises a trim sensor, and a direct current motor actuator connected to the trim tab cables. The sensor senses the differences in tension between the cables leading to the actuator by means of a polarity sensing switch. The resultant error signal is amplified, and then fed to the actuator motor causing it to displace the trim tab in the required direction.

Fig. 7.7. is a schematic representation of a control system adapted for trimming by means of a horizontal stabiliser of the type described on page 39. The trim servo in this application is a three-phase, dual-speed, dual-winding motor which operates in parallel with the elevator servomotor. When the automatic flight control system is engaged, the low-speed winding of the motor is supplied with three-phase, 115 volts alternating current at 400 Hz, via a power relay and a speed change relay. The motor drive shaft is also connected to two electromagnetic clutches which are energised by output voltage signals from the servo amplifier to which the elevator servomotor is connected. Depending on the phase of the signals, one or other of the clutches will engage the trim servomotor causing it either to raise or to lower the leading edge

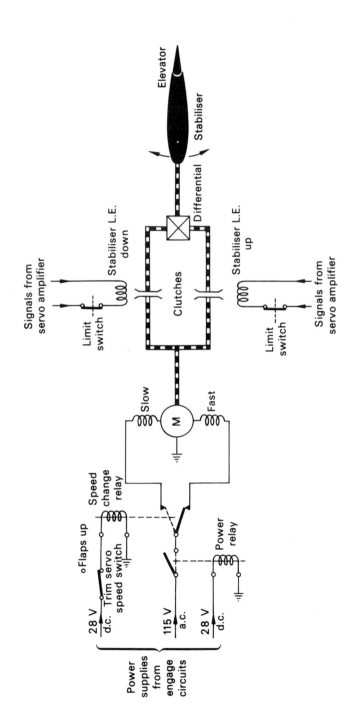

Fig. 7.7 Horizontal stabiliser trim control

of the stabiliser. Co-ordination between the elevator and stabiliser is obtained by the sensitivity of the trim servomotor being set so that the motor is only clutched to the stabiliser drive mechanism when the elevator servomotor delivers large amounts of torque. Thus, when the elevators are displaced to effect a pitch attitude change the stabiliser is displaced through a correspondingly smaller angle.

When the aircraft responds to the attitude change, and the elevator servomotor reverses direction to return the elevators to the streamlined position, the stabiliser remains at a certain angle as a result of the lower sensitivity of the trim servomotor. The stabiliser therefore provides the aircraft response necessary to establish the pitch trim required, and there is no need for manual trim when the automatic control system is engaged. In fact, the control system will automatically disconnect should manual trimming, or trimming via the main power actuator of the stabiliser, be carried out. The purpose of the limit switches shown in the trim signal circuits is to disengage the trim motor clutch solenoids in the event the stabiliser is driven beyond its travel limits in either the upward or downward direction. Two interlock microswitch assemblies (not shown in the diagram) are also incorporated in the trim servo unit, and they are activated by linear movement of the servomotor clutches during their engagement and disengagement. When both clutch solenoids are de-energised, or if either one is energised, the switches maintain a closed circuit. If, however, both solenoids are energised simultaneously, or if there is any type of switch malfunction, an open circuit condition will arise to disconnect the automatic flight control system.

When the flaps of an aircraft are lowered, the pitch attitude is changed and this must also be 'trimmed out' by the trim servo system. In the system just described, this is accomplished by selecting a trim servo speed switch to a 'flaps down' position. This causes the speed change relay to de-energise the relay in turn, completing a three-phase power supply circuit to the high-speed winding of the trim servomotor. In some cases (e.g. in the Boeing 737 system) the changeover to high speed operation of the motor is effected by switches actuated directly by the flaps.

Feedback

When a control command signal is supplied to a servomotor, its operation must be so regulated that it will apply corrective control proportional to a command signal input, and will limit the amount of applied control to prevent overshoot. It accomplishes this in accordance with closed-loop control servomechanism principles, i.e. it is designed to apply feedback such that the amplified signal to the servomotor is the algebraic sum of the attitude error signal and the feedback signal (see also chapter 2).

Assuming that an aircraft is subjected to a pitch-up displacement, an attitude error signal is produced commanding the pitch servomotor to apply down elevator. As the motor rotates, a feedback signal is produced in opposition to the error signal to reduce the error signal, and thereby limit the amount of servomotor rotation. The difference signal ensures proportionality of corrective control, and when the signals are equal, the error signal is reduced to zero and the servomotor stops rotating.

As the aircraft responds to the downward displacement of the elevators, the attitude sensing element now detects this as a nose-down disturbance, and produces a command signal accordingly. The servomotor now rotates in the opposite direction to start taking off elevator control as the aircraft flies into the level flight attitude. As before, a feedback signal is produced to reduce the error signal until rotation of the servomotor ceases, at which stage (and assuming that gain adjustments have been accurately made) the elevators will be in their neutral position, and the aircraft is again in the level flight attitude.

The methods adopted for producing feedback signals are dependent on the type of automatic flight control system, and on whether the system utilises position feedback or rate feedback. In general, either a potentiometric or a synchronous transmission method may be adopted for the production of position feedback, while a tachogenerator method is adopted for producing rate feedback. In some cases, the methods may be used in combination as a means of ensuring stabilisation of the complete feedback loop itself.

Yaw damping

All aircraft, particularly those having a swept-wing configuration, are subject to a yawing-rolling oscillation popularly known as 'Dutch Roll' (see page 25, chapter 1) but different aircraft show various degrees of damping, i.e. the inherent tendency to reduce the magnitude of oscillation and eventual return to straight flight varies. A sudden gust or a short uncoordinated rudder deflection produces a yawing motion, and this, in turn, initiates the Dutch Roll oscillation. The vertical stabiliser and the rudder (if kept in a fixed streamlined position) develop opposing forces that tend to offset the yawing motion, but as a result of the inertias of the aircraft's motions, stabilisation is regained in the form of a damped oscillation. As the aircraft recovers from the Dutch Roll, the magnitude of the oscillations gradually decreases. Thus, the Dutch Roll tendency may be comparatively mild in its effects and may, therefore, be tolerated without recourse to corrective action either manually or automatically.

For some aircraft, however, the natural damping of the Dutch Roll tendency is dependent not only on the size of the vertical stabiliser and rudder, but also on the aircraft's speed, the damping being more responsive at high speeds than at low speeds. It is, therefore, necessary in such cases for corrective action to be taken; such action requires displacement of the rudder in order to further assist the vertical stabiliser in its stabilising function, and is referred to as yaw damping.

In automatic flight control systems of the three-axis type, the rudder control channel, as we have already learned, is used primarily for coordinating a turn initiated via the aileron control channel, but in applying a three-axis control system to the type of aircraft just described, the rudder control channel may also provide for automatic yaw damping control. The control circuit is modified in such a way that if the aircraft is to be flown manually the complete rudder control channel, from yaw rate gyroscope sensing element to rudder servomotor, forms what is termed a yaw damper, and may be switched in independently of the other two channels of the automatic control system. Switching is done at the control panel, usually either by selecting a 'damper' position of the main engage switch (see fig. 2.11), or by actuating a separate yaw damper switch (see fig. 2.9).

Series yaw damper

In some types of aircraft, control of yaw damping is effected by a yaw damper system which, rather than forming a constituent part of the automatic flight control system, is designed to be independent from it. Other essential differences are that the yaw damper will not oppose rudder pedal movements made by the pilot in the normal manner, hence the term series (see also page 166), and it displaces the rudder by applying signals to the hydraulic power control unit of the rudder control system instead of to a rudder servomotor. The system employed in some Boeing 707 aircraft serves as a useful example for explaining the fundamentals of operation.

When the engage switch is placed in the 'on' position, electrical power is supplied to the coupler unit which contains a yaw rate gyroscope, and plug-in circuit modules relevant to filtering, synchronising, servo signal amplification, and gain calibration. Electrical power is also supplied to an 'engage' light, and a solenoid valve in the rudder power control unit, the valve allowing hydraulic pressure to the transfer valve. The yaw rate gyroscope actuates a pick-off element so that when any change about the yaw axis occurs, the signal produced is fed to a network which filters out all signals, except those characteristic of

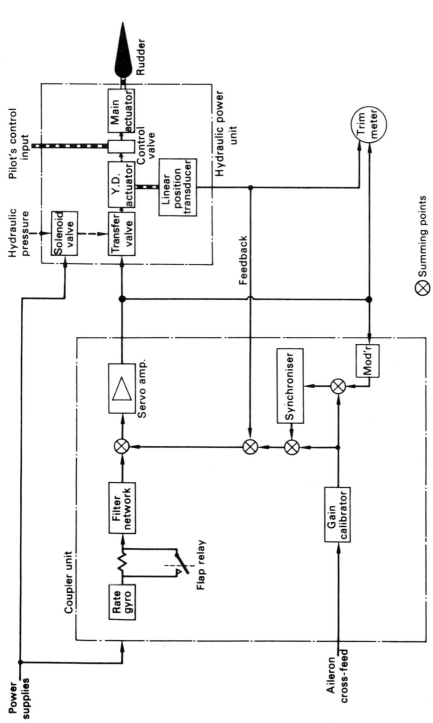

Fig. 7.8 Series yaw damper

Dutch Roll, for modulation and supply to a summing point. The output signal is then supplied to the servo amplifier and, after amplification, to the transfer valve which then allows hydraulic pressure to the yaw damper actuator; this, in turn, positions a valve which controls the pressure to one or other side of the piston in the main actuator. Thus, the rudder is moved in a direction to satisfy the command signal.

At the same time, the yaw damper actuator operates a linear position transducer, the function of which is to develop a feedback signal for summing with that of the filter output. It thereby provides the proper command signal to the transfer valve, and also 'nulls' the signal as a command is satisfied. The servo-amplifier output is also fed to a synchroniser network which synchronises any unbalance in the signal chain and, as will be noted from fig. 7.8, this output is also summed with the filter and feedback signals.

In order to compensate for differences in aerodynamic damping which arise between the landing flaps down and flaps up conditions, the yaw rate gyroscope output signal passes through a gain change circuit controlled by a relay that is operated by a flap position switch. The control is such that energising of the relay by-passes a resistance so as to produce a faster rate of response when the flaps are down.

Since the action of a series yaw damper is not felt at the rudder pedals, normal operation of the system is indicated to the pilot by deflections of the pointer of a rudder trim indicator connected in the actuator output signal circuit.

The automatic flight control system may be used in all modes with the yaw damper system engaged; however the associated interlock circuit prevents the use of the control system when the yaw damper is disengaged. When the control system is operating in the localiser mode, the yaw damper is supplied with signals from the aileron control channel through a cross-feed circuit.

Torque limiting

In flight, particularly where high rates of control are to be produced, the movement of the flight control surfaces can result in loads which may impose excessive stresses on the aircraft structure. It is necessary, therefore, under automatically-controlled flight conditions, to safeguard against such stresses, and furthermore to safeguard against a servomotor 'runaway' condition which would cause control surfaces to be displaced to their maximum hardover positions. Such safeguards are implemented by limiting the torque applied to the servomotors, and also by allowing them either to slip, or to be completely disengaged, in the event that preset torque limits are exceeded. The methods adopted usually depend on either mechanical, electrical. or electromechanical principles.

A schematic section view of a mechanical torque limiter is shown in fig. 7.9. It forms part of the mounting to which the servomotor is attached, and it utilises a ball and cone principle to provide slippage of clutch plates at a predetermined value of torque. It consists of input, intermediate and output members, the two former members being separated by balls and cones biased by spring 'B'. The clutch plates which form part of the intermediate and output members are biased together by means of spring 'A'. Under normal conditions of load, the torque applied to the input member by the servomotor is transmitted to the intermediate member via the balls and cones, and via the clutch plates to the output member and flight control system of the aircraft; a solid coupling is thus formed.

If the load conditions are above normal, the load torque on the

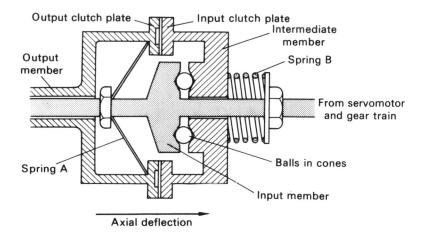

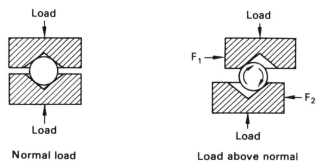

Fig. 7.9 Mechanical torque limiter

output member reacts with the torque of the input member. Shear forces 'F$_1$' and 'F$_2$' are thus applied to each set of cones tending to dislodge the balls from their seats, and so displace the cones at right-angles to the direction of the forces. As will be noted from the diagram, this causes the intermediate member to move away from the input member and so causes the clutch plates to slip. When load conditions revert to normal, the reaction of the shear forces decreases and the coupling between all three members again becomes a solid one under the action of spring 'B'.

A typical example of an electrically-operated torque limiting system is one which is applied to a type of servomotor using a two-phase induction motor. In this case a resistor is connected in series with the control phase of the motor to limit the torque by lowering the control phase voltage. Two limit switches are also connected in series with the reference phase of the motor so that, when the preset torque limit is reached, the switches are actuated such that they interrupt the supply to the reference phase. Further rotation of the servomotor is thereby prevented.

An example of an electro-mechanical type of torque limiter is shown schematically in fig. 7.10. The unit operates in conjunction with the electromagnetic clutch of the servomotor, and in the clutch engaged position (diagram *a*) the drive from the motor is transmitted via a spring-loaded cam and roller assembly, and a driving slot which engages with a cam-follower. If the torque at the output shaft exceeds the torque determined by the springs, the input gear turns relative to the output gear and the cam rollers ride up the cam slopes (diagram *b*). This action forces the cam and driving slot to move against the pressure of the springs, and after a specified movement the cam makes contact with the operating pin of a switch whose contacts are opened to interrupt the power supply to the clutch solenoid. In this condition the input drive is disconnected, and the springs are permitted to force the cam back to its normal operating position, i.e. with the cam rollers in the detent of the cam. The switch operating pin returns to its normal position and the switch contacts close, but re-engagement of the clutch is prevented by a relay holding the clutch circuit open.

If the clutch fails to disengage when the switch is operated, the input gear continues to turn relative to the output gear and the cam rollers ride further up the cam slopes until they move over the tops of the cam and drop into recesses (diagram *c*). When this occurs, the springs force the cam upwards to such an extent that the cam driving slot is dis-engaged from its rollers on the output shaft. The upward movement of the cam further operates the switch such that its contacts remain in the open position to prevent re-engagement of the servomotor with the aircraft's flight control system.

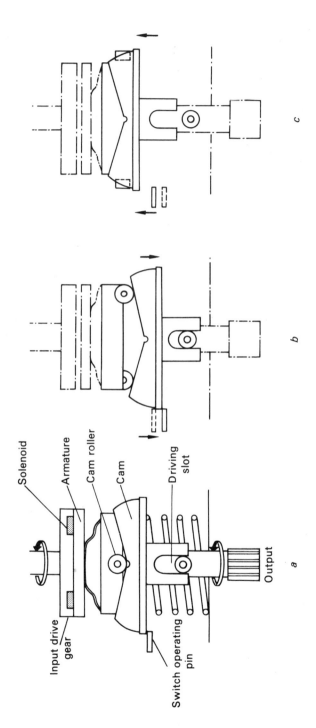

Fig. 7.10 Electro-mechanical torque limiter

Phase advance

Phase advance refers to a method adopted in some automatic flight control systems as a means of providing powered control that will ensure maximum damping of an aircraft's response to the applied control. In order to understand why this is necessary, the response of an aircraft to disturbances should be considered.

Assuming that an aircraft is disturbed in pitch, inertia will momentarily carry it forward in the displaced attitude. The airflow over the aircraft acts on the tail of the aircraft and, because of the longitudinal moment arm and natural damping, a turning force about the centre of gravity is produced causing the aircraft to return to its normal attitude. Displacement of the elevators in the appropriate direction increases the turning force and therefore causes the aircraft to respond more quickly. Thus there are, in effect, two forces available for restoring an aircraft to its normal attitude; the natural damping force, and the additional force created by the use of flight control surfaces.

The damping force is a variable depending on the aircraft type and, in some cases, it is of such a low magnitude that the aircraft in responding to control surface displacement may oscillate about a mean attitude. The effect as appropriate to a disturbance producing a pitch-up displacement is shown in fig. 7.11 *a*. At point 'A', the displacement is produced and down-elevator is applied to correct the disturbance. The aircraft responds to the elevator displacement (points 'B' to 'C') and during this stage elevator control is progressively taken off, until at point 'C' the normal attitude has been regained with zero control applied. The inertial effect of an aircraft with low natural damping causes it to overshoot the normal attitude, while up-elevator is being applied for correction purposes (points 'C' to 'D'). At point 'D', the aircraft is responding to up-elevator control and is once more approaching the normal attitude.

If the oscillation is to be prevented, then it will be appreciated that during the stage 'B' to 'C' it is not sufficient to take off the applied control, but that opposite control should be applied as the point 'C' is approached, as shown in diagram *b*. Thus, at point 'A' the control surface is moved to a maximum value to counteract the pitch-up displacement, and from this point to point 'B', control is being taken off and the rate of change of aircraft attitude is decreasing. As the aircraft starts returning to its normal attitude (point 'B') so elevator control is taken off completely, and is applied in the opposite direction to prevent overshoot (points 'B' to 'C').

If the disturbance control and the damping control are referenced to the same time base then, as will be observed from fig. 7.11 *c*, the damping control is advanced in phase with respect to the disturbance

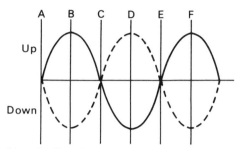

a Aircraft disturbance and control movement

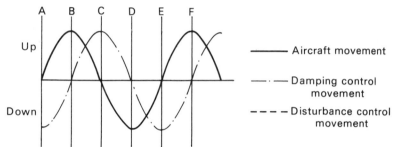

—————— Aircraft movement

—·—· Damping control movement

— — — Disturbance control movement

b Aircraft and damping control movement

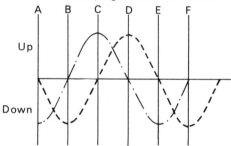

c Disturbance and damping control movement

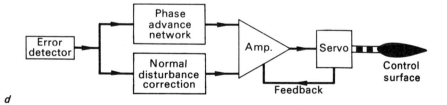

d

Fig. 7.11 Phase advance

control. The required control for a given disturbance is, therefore, the algebraic sum of both controls, and in any given automatic flight control system they may be applied as components of the signals from the attitude error detecting elements as shown in diagram *d* of fig. 7.11.

For explanatory purposes, the phase advance has been assumed to have a phase angle of 90°. It should be noted, however, that this angle will vary from one aircraft to another, and even from one control surface to another on the same aircraft, e.g. the pitch damping requirement on a given aircraft will be very different from the yaw damping requirement.

The phase-advancing methods adopted in automatic flight control systems vary between systems, but the method adopted in the Bendix

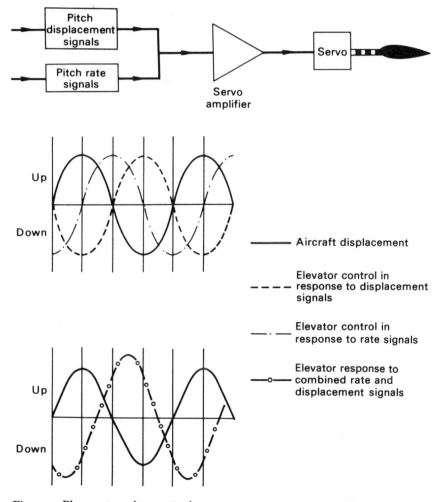

Fig. 7.12 Phase advancing method

PB20 serves as a useful example. In this system, two detector signals are fed into the pitch control channel servo amplifiers, one such signal being derived from the pitch rate gyroscope and therefore being proportional to the rate of pitch change, while the other signal is derived from a vertical gyroscope and is proportional to pitch displacement. Both signals are combined as shown in fig. 7.12, to produce an algebraic response in which the aircraft control is phase-advanced with respect to the disturbance.

Trim indicators

In most automatic flight control systems, a trim indicator is provided, its functions being to indicate that signals are being supplied to the servomotors, whether in the engaged or disengaged condition, and also to indicate any out-of-trim conditions of the aircraft under normal operating conditions of the control system. It performs these functions by monitoring the outputs from the rudder, aileron and elevator servo amplifiers, and by producing deflections of pointers from zero datum marks in response to signals supplied. Two examples of three-channel trim indicators designed for mounting on instrument panels are shown in fig. 7.13. In some control systems, monitoring of the elevator channel only is carried out, the appropriate indicators being incorporated in the flight control panels.

The pointers, which symbolise the flight control surfaces, are actuated by d.c. milliammeters, and are deflected each time servo amplifier signals are supplied to the servomotors. When the signals are balanced out as a result of servo control commands being satisfied, the pointers return to their zero 'trimmed' positions. In the event that a servo amplifier produces a continuous correction signal in order to maintain aircraft attitude, then the appropriate pointer will be continuously deflected as an indication that the aircraft is out-of-trim.

In systems which incorporate aileron and elevator position transmitters, signals from the latter are always present when the automatic control system is powered but disengaged. Thus, whenever the control column and/or the control wheel is moved, the associated trim indicator pointers will also be displaced.

The indicator shown in the lower part of fig. 7.13, also incorporates three indicators which display the word IN to signify that each servomotor is engaged.

Fig. 7.13 Trim indicators

Mach trim system

In aircraft that are subject to the effect known as 'tuck-under' (see page 45) the automatic flight control system, when engaged, automatically senses the attitude change and re-adjusts the position of the horizontal stabiliser and elevators, to maintain pitch trim of the aircraft. In order to compensate for the effect under manually-controlled flight conditions, however, it is usual to provide an additional system which is designed to position the stabiliser as a function of Mach number, and so provide a positive control column force gradient; such a system is referred to as a Mach Trim System.

The system depends for its operation on signals derived initially from a synchro which may be integrated with the pitot-static pressure sensing element of a Machmeter or of a separate Mach transmitter. The synchro is connected to a receiver synchro to form a closed loop system. When the speed of the aircraft reaches, and remains in excess of, a pre-determined Mach number (a typical value is 0.8 Mach) the synchro loop signal operates a servomotor which drives the wiper of a potentiometer. The variable output from the potentiometer is then amplified and fed to an auto-trim actuator (see also page 174) which rotates to drive the leading edge of the horizontal stabiliser down thereby trimming the aircraft to fly 'nose up'. In order to ensure proportionality between stabiliser movement and aircraft speed changes above the pre-determined value, a follow-up signal is fed into the actuator control circuit from a synchro transmitter mechanically actuated by the stabiliser.

8
Flight Director and Integrated Flight Control Systems

Flight instrument evolution has followed a pattern of divergent display complexity with advancing technology followed by consolidation of the displays as human capabilities of data interpretation were exceeded. Initially, instrument panel space was devoted to the minimum instrumentation needed for the control of the aircraft, i.e. the turn and slip indicator and the airspeed indicator. Also present were essential engine data displays, and the fundamental attitude data displays provided by the gyro horizon, the barometric type altimeter, vertical speed indicator, and the magnetic compass. Even at this low level of complexity, problems associated with interpretation of displayed data, scanning of instruments and accuracy were manifest. Many diverse panel arrangements came into use, reflecting the vagaries of particular instrument manufacturers, of demands on panel shape and size, and of the experience of particular pilots under instrument flying conditions.

Although the minimum instrumentation referred to above provided the essential data to manoeuvre and control the aircraft, instrument flight was feasible only as an emergency measure for relatively short periods. However point-to-point navigation, with the precision needed for both military and public transport operations, required the development of new flight instruments and navigational aids. This eventually came about with the progressive development of such radio navigation systems as automatic direction finder (ADF), ILS, VOR, and distance measuring equipment. While it was possible, and practical, to navigate by the earlier developed systems, a high degree of pilot proficiency was nevertheless demanded. This was particularly evident during the terminal manoeuvring and approach-to-landing phase, where the most precise flight path control is required coincident with the performance of many other tasks preparatory to landing.

In order to ease the pilot's workload, and to achieve greater precision of flight guidance and control, the idea of presenting data in the form of control commands was conceived, and this led ultimately to the application of servomechanism design principles to systems known as flight directors.

A pioneer flight director system (FDS) was the Zero Reader (developed by Sperry) which sensed not only flight path deviation, but also such control parameters as aircraft attitude, attitude rate, and deviation rate. Control command signals were computed and presented on an indicator not unlike that of the ILS. Although the pilot no longer had to assemble basic control data from a number of instruments, it was still necessary for him to monitor continuously other instruments as an assurance that all parameters were consistent and compatible with the desired flight objective.

It was logical, therefore, in the next stage of development, to integrate functions of a flight director with those of the complementary instruments, so that essential data could be displayed on fewer instruments thereby reducing scanning time. With small variations from one application to another, and from one aircraft operator to another, this basic integration concept is adopted in a majority of today's aircraft, despite the added demands stemming from the progress in operating under reduced visibility, and in the development of new navigation equipment. The lowering of weather minima (see page 200) directly affects instruments complexity as a result of the need for additional display functions, such as redundant and expanded flight path deviation, airspeed deviation, radio altitude, de-crab and roll-out command data, and integration of turn-and-slip data into the primary display. The advancement to lower weather minima created the need for display integrity; this, in turn, required that nearly all the functions of the instruments be monitored, and that provision be made for the warning of faulty display functions. The demands created by the development of new navigation equipment result from technical innovation and added flexibility. There is a need to assimilate navigational data not previously available or which is now available in a new form. Furthermore, there is a need to indicate which type of system is generating the displayed information, in which mode that system is operating, which of several redundant sets of that type of equipment is connected, and in what co-ordinates the data is displayed.

In the field of automatic flight control, the development of control systems was also strongly influenced by the demands imposed on flight director systems, particularly for control in all phases of flight. The principal reason for this is that much of the basic attitude and navigational data is common to both systems. It was also logical, therefore, to expand on the concept of integration, such that data and servomechanism links could be shared, that a flight director system could provide guidance commands for an automatic flight control system and monitor its performance, and be available for reversion to effective manual control if fully automatic control should be lost. Because so much of the basic data and system hardware can be shared, flight director systems are usually developed and made available as a natural complement to each manufacturer's automatic flight control system.

A flight director system developed in this manner comprises two principal display units: they are variously called (i) flight director, attitude flight director or an approach horizon; and (ii) a course deviation indicator or horizontal situation indicator. A number of display configurations may be adopted dependent on a particular manufacturer's design, and on the extent of the functions to be integrated. However, there are certain features which are of a common nature and these may be highlighted by considering the two units shown in figs. 8.1 and 8.2.

The flight director presents aircraft attitude and direction information in the form of a three-dimensional display. Attitude is displayed by the relationship of a stationary delta-shaped symbol representing the aircraft, with respect to roll and pitch commands displayed by two pointers, or command bars flanking the aircraft symbol, and also by a horizon bar. The command bars form a shallow inverted 'V', and are driven by separate servomotors within the indicator such that they move up and down to command a change in pitch, and rotate clockwise and anti-clockwise to command a change of roll attitude. The outputs of the two servos are combined mechanically so as to provide an integrated pitch and roll command. Sensing with respect to the aircraft symbol is such that the pilot is always directed to 'fly into the V'. When a command has been satisfied, the command bars are aligned with the edges of the aircraft symbol.

The horizon bar is carried on a flexible tape which is also driven by separate pitch and roll servomotors within the indicator. Freedom of tape movement in pitch is $\pm 90°$, and 360° in roll. The upper and lower sections of the tape are coloured to represent the sky and ground respectively, and they also have index marks on them to indicate pitch angles. In some types of flight director, the lower section of the moving tape is also marked with lines converging on the centre of the indicator display thereby enhancing its 'forward view' effect. Roll angle is displayed by a pointer which rotates with the flexible tape, and is referenced against a fixed scale. The servomotors are supplied with signals from a vertical gyroscope unit located at a remote point.

Deviations from the ILS glide slope beam (see also page 147) are shown by vertical displacements of a pointer over a scale at the left-hand side of the indicator display. Each of the inner dots on the scale represents a $\frac{1}{4}°$ displacement from the beam centre line, while the outer

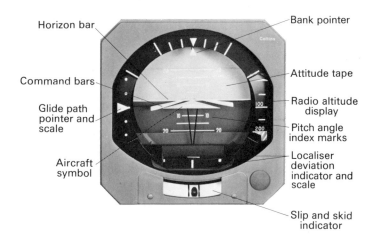

Horizon bar
Bank pointer
Command bars
Attitude tape
Glide path pointer and scale
Radio altitude display
Pitch angle index marks
Aircraft symbol
Localiser deviation indicator and scale
Slip and skid indicator

Fig. 8.1 Flight director indicator

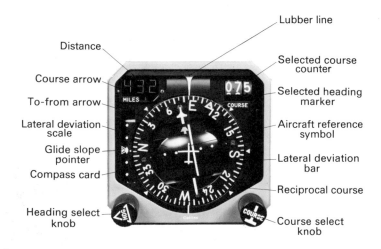

Lubber line
Distance
Selected course counter
Course arrow
To-from arrow
Selected heading marker
Lateral deviation scale
Aircraft reference symbol
Glide slope pointer
Lateral deviation bar
Compass card
Reciprocal course
Heading select knob
Course select knob

Fig. 8.2 Course indicator

dots each represents a $\frac{1}{2}°$ displacement. The pointer is driven by a d.c. meter movement and, when not in use, is deflected out of view at the top of the scale. A pointer at the lower part of the display indicates deviations from the localiser beam, and is shaped to symbolise a view of a runway during an approach. The reference dots on the localiser or runway scale, indicate approximately $1\frac{1}{4}°$ displacement from the beam centre line. The pointer is also driven by a d.c. meter movement, and, when not in use, is obscured by a black warning flag as shown in fig. 8.1. In some types of indicator, the localiser pointer, or runway symbol, is also displaced in response to signals from a radio altimeter so that during the last 200 feet of descent, the pointer moves up to the fixed aircraft symbol thereby presenting a 'live' display of the approach. This radio altitude display concept is also adopted in the indicator shown in fig. 8.1, but, in this case, it is effected by a pointer moving over a fixed altitude scale.

Indications of slip or skid are provided by an inclinometer similar to that adopted in conventional turn and slip indicators. In addition, some flight directors have a rate of turn pointer incorporated in the display, the pointer being actuated by signals from a rate gyroscope sensor unit.

Another command function which may be displayed in some flight directors, is that related to the speed of an aircraft when executing a go-around manoeuvre following a missed approach. The display comprises a vertical scale and a pointer which is actuated in response to signals corresponding to the difference between indicated airspeed and a pre-determined go-around speed obtained from a speed computing system external to the flight director. The scale has several graduations ranging from the computed speed at the centre, to 'fast' and 'slow' at the top and bottom of the scale respectively. In order to achieve the correct go-around speed, engine power is adjusted so as to maintain the pointer at the centre of the scale. The pilot selects the go-around mode by pressing a button switch on the control wheel, the selection being indicated by the illumination of an annunciator light marked 'GA', and by displacement of the flight director command bars to command a wings-level climb attitude. In association with the go-around mode, a second annunciator light marked 'MDA' (minimum decision altitude) is provided. The light illuminates when the aircraft has descended to the preset radio altitude at which the decision whether to land or go-around must be made. If a flight director system is supplying guidance commands to an automatic flight control system during an approach, the latter system (with the exception of one having automatic landing capability) is caused to disengage when the 'GA' mode is selected.

The internal circuit arrangement of a representative type of flight director indicator is shown in fig. 8.3.

A course deviation indicator presents a pictorial display of a navigation situation and, as will be noted from fig. 8.2, the situation is shown as a plan view of the aircraft's position and heading with respect to a selected heading and course. The alternative name of horizontal situation indicator is thus aptly applied. In addition to magnetic heading data signals, the indicator is also supplied with signal inputs corresponding to deviations from an ILS localiser beam, and VOR radial, and from a glide path beam. Indication of flight either to or from a VOR station is also provided. Selector knobs at the

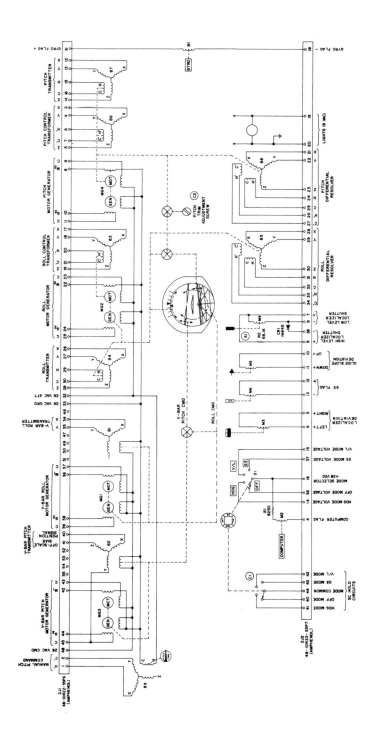

Fig. 8.3 Flight director indicator circuit arrangement

bottom corners of the indicator permit the setting of a desired magnetic heading and a VOR or localiser course. The aircraft reference symbol is fixed at the centre of the display and it indicates the position and heading of the aircraft in relation to the compass or azimuth card, and the lateral deviation bar. The compass card is synchronous-linked with the aircraft's magnetic compass system, and when changes in aircraft heading take place a position error signal is produced in a control transformer synchro within the indicator. After amplification by a servo amplifier in the instrument amplifier unit, the signal is supplied to a servomotor which, by means of a gear train system, drives the compass card to indicate the new heading with reference to a lubber line at the top centre of the indicator. Card movement is damped by means of a rate feedback signal produced by a rate generator which is driven by the motor. Feedback signals are mixed with position error signals, and the composite signal is amplified and supplied to the control phase of the servomotor.

At the same time, the servomotor drives the control transformer synchro rotor to the null position corresponding to the new heading. The lateral deviation bar is a movable centre section of the course arrow, and represents the centre line of the selected localiser course or VOR radial. The bar is deflected to the left or right by a d.c. meter movement to indicate the appropriate commands necessary for beam interception and capture, and it also rotates with the compass card as changes in aircraft heading take place. When operating in the localiser mode, initial movement of the deviation bar begins when the aircraft is approximately $4°$ from the localiser beam centre, and the dots on the deviation scale represent approximately $1\frac{1}{4}°$ and $2\frac{1}{2}°$ from beam centre. In the VOR mode, initial movement of the bar begins when the aircraft is approximately $16°$ from radial centre, and the deviation scale dots then represent approximately $5°$ and $10°$ from radial centre.

Selection of a desired localiser course or VOR radial, is carried out by rotating the course selector knob until the course arrow coincides with the desired value on the compass card. The lateral deviation bar and deviation scale also rotate with the course arrow through the gear train system driven by the selector knob. At the same time a digital type of course counter is driven to the corresponding course indication; in fig. 8.2, this is displayed as $075°$. Once set, the course arrow rotates with the compass card as aircraft heading changes. The gear train system also positions the rotors of a course resolver synchro associated with the VOR/LOC navigation receiver, and of a course datum control transformer synchro. When the course resolver synchro rotor position is changed, it shifts the phase of the reference 30 Hz signal in a phase shift circuit of the VOR instrumentation unit. The signal is then compared with the variable 30 Hz signal in a phase comparator, the output of which is supplied to the meter movement controlling the lateral deviation bar. When the output is such that it centres the deviation bar the aircraft is on the course selected.

When the aircraft deviates from the selected course, the phase-shifted reference signal is maintained at the angle determined by the resolver synchro rotor, but the variable signal phase received by the VOR navigation receiver is changed. The phase comparator will then produce an output which deflects the deviation bar to the left or right of the selected VOR course. The to–from arrow is positioned by a meter movement which is supplied with the corresponding signals from the radio navigation receiver and via a phase comparator in the instrumentation unit of the flight director system. In fig. 8.2 a 'fly to' command is displayed. In the LOC mode of operation, the deviation bar is similarly controlled by changes in resolver synchro rotor position, except that the output to the meter movement results from amplitude comparison of the signals either side of localiser beam centre. The to–from arrows remain out of view since no to–from signals are transmitted in the localiser mode.

Changes in the position of the course datum control transformer synchro rotor produces a position error signal in the stator windings. The signal is proportional to the difference between the selected course and the actual heading of the aircraft and is transmitted to the roll control channel of a steering computer or a flight director computer as a turn command to capture the selected VOR/LOC course. The signal is also transmitted to the automatic flight control system and if this system is coupled to the flight director, it will, of course, turn the aircraft automatically. The output from the appropriate computer is supplied to a roll command servo amplifier contained in an instrument amplifier unit, and after amplification it is fed to the roll servomotor coupled to the command bars of the flight director. Thus, the bars rotate to indicate the direction of roll required to capture the VOR/LOC course. The servomotor also drives a rate generator which produces a rate feedback signal for the purpose of damping display movements.

The selection of any desired magnetic heading is accomplished by positioning a triangular-shaped heading marker over the compass card, by means of the heading selector knob and its associated shaft and gear train system. At the same time, the rotor of a heading error control transformer synchro is rotated inside its stator, from its null position, and this produces a position error signal proportional to the difference between the selected heading and aircraft heading sensed by the compass system. In fig. 8.2, the headings displayed are respectively 110° and 085°. The signal is processed in the same manner as that produced by the course datum control transformer synchro, and therefore results in the flight director command bars indicating the direction of roll required to fly on the desired heading. The circuit arrangement of a representative type of course indicator is illustrated in fig. 8.4.

As noted earlier, provision must be made for the warning of faulty display functions. In practice, warnings are effected by monitoring the command signals produced, so that when they are lost or are too weak to provide reliable information small red flags appear at appropriate parts of the flight director indicator and course indicator displays. The flags are actuated by d.c. meter mechanisms which are connected to the relevant signal sources.

In the case of flight director indicators there are, primarily, three warning flags labelled 'GS', 'GYRO' and 'COMPUTER' and respectively they indicate malfunctions of the glide-slope receiver or signal, the vertical gyroscope and attitude display systems, and the director or steering computer and command display systems. The GS flag, when indicating a malfunction, obscures the glide slope pointer and scale to prevent its use. If the system is not being operated in the glide slope mode, the GS flag and pointer are biassed off-scale. Indication of localiser signal malfunction and/or localiser mode not selected, is also provided and generally takes the form of a black shutter which obscures the localiser pointer and scale (see fig. 8.1).

Other warning flags may be provided depending on any additional functions displayed; for example, a flag is provided to give warning of malfunctions in the circuit of a speed control display associated with a go-around manoeuvre.

In the case of a course indicator, there are also three primary warning flags and these are labelled 'GS', 'COMPASS' and 'VOR/LOC'. The GS flag operates in the same manner as that provided in the flight director indicator, while the compass flag indicates malfunctions of the magnetic heading signal circuit of the compass system. The VOR/LOC flag serves the dual function of warning of VOR radial signal and localiser signal malfunction. Warning flag operation is summarised in the table on page 202.

In some types of flight director systems, a pitch command facility is provided which permits the pilot to preselect a fixed climb or descent command under certain modes of operation. Selection is carried out by means of a selector knob which, in some cases, is located in the bottom left-hand corner of a flight director indicator (see fig. 8.5) and in others is located on a separate flight director mode selector panel. The selector knob is mechanically coupled to the rotor of a control transformer synchro, and after the knob is rotated a signal is induced in the synchro. After amplification, this signal is transmitted to the pitch servomotor/generator which drives the command bars to the

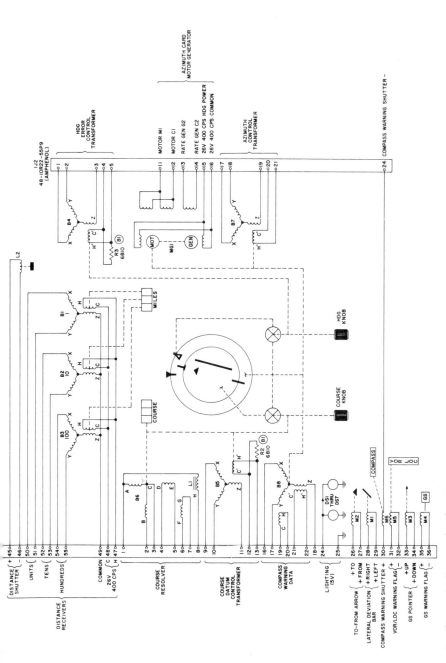

Fig. 8.4 Course indicator circuit arrangement

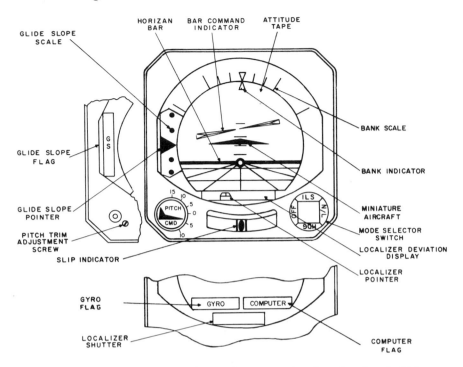

Fig. 8.5 Flight director indicator with pitch command and mode select facilities

selected position. The aircraft attitude is then changed by 'flying the aircraft symbol into the command bars'. In addition to pitch command, a pitch trim adjustment is provided as a means of altering the position of the flight director horizon bar with respect to the aircraft symbol. The adjustment is purely mechanical in operation and is used for aligning the attitude display during installation of a flight director.

A number of flight director systems incorporate facilities for selecting various modes of operation, such facilities being comparable in function to the outer loop control of an automatic flight control system. This being so, it is possible for mode selection to be used on a common basis in cases where a flight director system is employed in combination with an automatic flight control system. The number of modes vary dependent on specific aircraft operating requirements, and for a similar reason, the method by which modes are selected can also vary; for example, selection may be effected by the control knob of a rotary selector switch on a flight director indicator (see fig. 8.5), or on a separate mode selector panel (see fig. 8.6).

In some versions of a control panel, shown in fig. 8.7, modes are selected by push buttons which are push-on/push-off solenoid-hold switches. The push buttons illuminate when their corresponding modes

FLIGHT DIRECTOR INDICATOR ‑‑‑ COURSE INDICATOR

MODE	SIGNALS CONTROLLING COMMAND V-BARS — ROLL	PITCH	HORIZON ATTITUDE DISPLAY	GLIDE-SLOPE DEVIATION POINTER	LOCALIZER DEVIATION POINTER	WARNING FLAGS — GLIDE-SLOPE	LOCALIZER	GYRO	COMPUTER	(CI) GLIDE-SLOPE DEVIATION POINTER	VOR/LOC DEVIATION BAR	WARNING FLAGS — GLIDE-SLOPE	VOR/LOC	COMPASS	TO-FROM ARROW
OFF	BIASED OUT OF VIEW	OUT OF VIEW	SHOWS PITCH & ROLL	OUT OF VIEW UNLESS TUNED TO ILS – THEN SHOWS GLIDE-SLOPE DEVIATION	COVERED BY FLAG	OUT OF VIEW UNLESS TUNED TO ILS – THEN MONITORS ILS RADIO	COVERS DISPLAY		BIASED OUT OF VIEW	OUT OF VIEW UNLESS TUNED TO ILS – THEN SHOWS GLIDE-SLOPE DEVIATION					OUT OF VIEW UNLESS RADIO TUNED TO VOR – THEN DISPLAYS TO-FROM
HDG	HEADING ERROR + BANK ATTITUDE	PITCH COMMAND + PITCH ATTITUDE						MONITORS GYRO + SERVO POWER + SERVO ERROR	MONITORS COMPASS + GYRO + COMPUTER						
VOR/LOC RADIO TUNED TO VOR	VOR RADIO DEVIATION + BANK + COURSE DATUM								MONITORS COMPASS + GYRO + VOR RADIO + COMPUTER	OUT OF VIEW	DISPLAYS VOR/LOC DEVIATION	OUT OF VIEW UNLESS TUNED TO ILS – THEN MONITORS ILS RADIO	MONITORS NAV RADIO	MONITORS COMPASS + SERVO POWER + SERVO ERROR	DISPLAYS TO-FROM
VOR/LOC RADIO TUNED TO LOC	LOCALIZER RADIO DEVIATION + BANK + COURSE DATUM				INDICATES LOCALIZER DEVIATION	MONITORS GLIDE-SLOPE RADIO	MONITORS LOCALIZER RADIO		MONITORS COMPASS + GYRO + LOC RADIO + COMPUTER						
GS	LOCALIZER RADIO DEVIATION + BANK + COURSE DATUM	PITCH ATTITUDE + GLIDE-SLOPE RADIO DEVIATION		INDICATES GLIDE-SLOPE DEVIATION		MONITORS GLIDE-SLOPE RADIO	MONITORS LOCALIZER RADIO		MONITORS COMPASS + GYRO + LOC RADIO + GS RADIO + COMPUTER	INDICATES GLIDE-SLOPE DEVIATION		MONITORS GLIDE-SLOPE RADIO			OUT OF VIEW

Fig. 8.6 Mode selector panel

Fig. 8.7 Push-button type mode selector

are selected and at the same time a mechanically-actuated flag with the word 'ON' appears over a portion of each button engaged. The operating modes which are fundamental to some typical flight director systems, are briefly described in the table below, while some appropriate display indications are summarised in the table on page 201. When each mode is selected, signal circuits are completed through the appropriate computer and amplifier sections, the outputs of which are supplied as command signals to the flight director indicator. If a flight director system is used in combination with an automatic flight control system, the command signals are also utilised by this sytem for applying control in the sense necessary to satisfy the relevant commands.

Fundamental Operating Modes

OFF   Command bars deflected out of sight, and flight director indicator used as an attitude reference only.

HDG	Command bars provide lateral guidance to achieve and maintain a compass heading, as selected on the course indicator. Vertical guidance is from a preselected pitch attitude.
VOR(NAV)/LOC	Command bars provide lateral guidance to capture and track a VOR radial or localiser beam. Vertical guidance is the same as in HDG mode.
GS	Command bars provide lateral and vertical guidance to capture and track the localiser and glide slope beams respectively. The GS and LOC pointers monitor aircraft deviations of the beam.
GS AUTO	As for GS except that interception and capture of glide slope takes place automatically after the localiser beam has been captured.
ALT	Command bars provide vertical guidance to hold the aircraft at the desired altitude.
APPR I	Selected for capture and tracking of GS and LOC beams on ILS approaches to Category I standards (see page 209). Command bars provide lateral and vertical guidance.
APPR II	As for APPR I but produces tighter tracking of beams to meet higher precision requirements of a Category II ILS approach (see page 209).
GA	Selected for a go-around manoeuvre after a missed approach, and after selecting either one of the approach modes. The command bars command a wings-level, pitch-up attitude. HDG and IAS modes may be selected after go-around power settings and airspeed are established.
IAS	Selected to maintain a particular indicated airspeed during climbout after take-off, and during letdown over a VOR station. The command bars provide vertical guidance.

V/S	Selected to maintain a particular vertical speed, i.e. rate of climb or descent. The command bars provide vertical guidance.
MACH	As for IAS mode but selected at higher altitudes.

As already noted in the foregoing brief descriptions of flight director indicator and course indicator operation, the appropriate command signals are processed by computer and instrument amplifier units. The primary function of a computer unit is to provide all the computation necessary for determining any position or attitude errors, and to develop the signals necessary to command position or attitude changes. When a flight director system is integrated with an automatic flight control system, the computed signals are also utilised for the application of control. A computer may in some cases be a single unit containing solid-state signal circuits for both lateral and vertical guidance information, while for some director systems separate computer units are utilised. In addition to the signal circuits, a logic network is incorporated, its purpose being to provide correct analogue scaling of signals, and to adjust computer gains and logic to suit specific types of aircraft. All signal and power supply circuits are on printed circuit boards which are arranged as separate functional plug-in modules.

The primary function of an instrument amplifier is to supply servo-actuating power for the display mechanisms of the flight director and course indicators. The unit also contains separate plug-in module circuit boards which, as shown in the overall signal flow diagram of a representative system (fig. 8.8) correspond to five servo channels, two signal converter channels, and three flag alarm circuits. If additional warnings are required the number of alarm circuits is increased accordingly. The converter channels accept d.c. input signals and convert them to 400 Hz signals for use by the pitch and roll command servo channels. The converters receive pitch and roll steering signals from the computer, position error signal information from the pitch and roll command control transformer synchros in the flight director, and rate feedback signals from the pitch and roll command servomotor/ generators. These signals are mixed and, after filtering, the composite signals provide the input for the appropriate command servo amplifier.

The continuing development of flight director systems, notably in the reduction of separate components, is typified by the example shown in fig. 8.9. In this case both indicators and the amplifier and computer units are housed in a single panel-mounted unit.

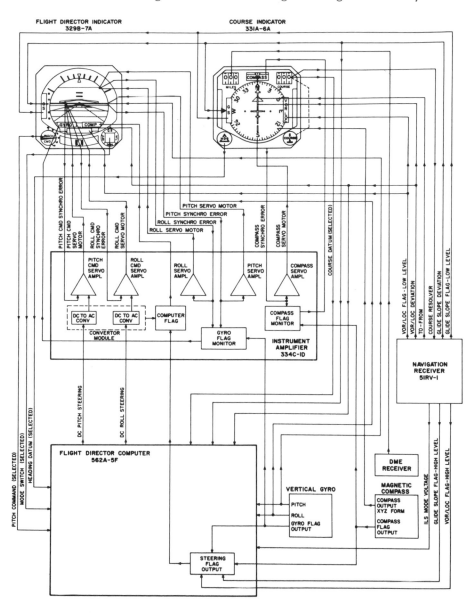

Fig. 8.8 Signal flow diagram of a representative system

Fig. 8.9 Combined flight director system units

9
Automatic Landing

The fundamental landing requirement

In order to achieve a safe landing, an aircraft has to be so controlled that its wheels make contact with the ground comfortably within the paved surface of the runway, within fairly narrow longitudinal limits along it, and at a sinking speed not greatly in excess of an optimum value of about 1 to 2 feet per second. The speed at touch-down should have been reduced from the approach margin of about 30% above the stall to about half this value, by progressive reduction of engine power during the landing flare. Finally, the wings should have been levelled prior to the actual landing, and the aircraft yawed to bring its longitudinal axis parallel to the runway centre-line to remove any drift angle due to cross-wind; the latter manoeuvre being known as decrabbing, or drift 'kick-off'. Control of the aircraft is needed about all three axes simultaneously, as well as the control of airspeed through engine power changes; it will be appreciated, therefore, that the approach and landing manoeuvre is the most difficult one demanded of the pilot. Add to this the unfortunate fact that in aircraft operations a large percentage of all accidents can be attributed to the approach and landing phase of a flight, and it is self-evident that systems designed to carry out automatic landings under all visibility conditions must provide guidance and control better than that provided by the pilot looking at the outside world. Accident rate statistics figure largely in the formulation of the requirements for automatic landing systems, and this led to the adoption (by the United Kingdom certification authorities) of a minimum reliability value of 1 in 10^7; in other words, that a system should not cause a fatal accident more often than one in ten million landings.

The control function during the approach and landing manoeuvre is required on a highly repetitive basis, and although a number of parameters are to be controlled simultaneously, such control is only necessary for a comparatively short period of time, and is therefore most suited to automatic means.

As a prelude to 'blind landing', automatic landing has always been the ultimate aim of control systems designers and aircraft operators, throughout the development of automatic flight control systems. The history of such developments, the attendant problems, and the attainment of the requisite high safety levels have been so well documented over the past two decades that even a brief summary would constitute a volume in itself. However, in making a broad analysis of available data, it will be found that the many problems which have had to be solved in the development of systems in current use, and having autolanding capability, can be grouped in the following three main areas.

1. Achieving the highest integrity and reliability of systems bearing in mind that they need to be entrusted with very considerable authority over the controls of an aircraft, including the throttles, and in the presence of the ground.

2. The provision of adequate monitoring information on the progress of the approach and landing manoeuvre, and which will enable the pilot to take over under the most critical conditions of a system malfunction in the presence of the ground.

3. The substitution of the pilot's direct vision with an automatic ground guidance system, having an integrity and reliability of the same high order as that demanded of the 'on board' system.

Weather minima

In low visibility operations, the weather limits for landing are given in the following terms.

1. *Runway visual range* (RVR) which is an instrumentally derived value that represents the range at which high-intensity lights can be seen in the direction of landing along the runway. Its readings are transmitted to the air traffic controller who can inform the pilot of the very latest visibility conditions.

2. *Decision height* which is that below which the pilot must not descend unless, in his estimation, he can see sufficient of the ground to continue the approach safely and land by visual judgement.

Minimum values of these two quantities (known as 'weather minima') are specified by the national licensing authorities for various types of aircraft, and for various airports. When the traffic controller advises that RVR is above the specified minimum the pilot may descend to the specified decision height, and if by then he has sighted a sufficiently large segment of the ground to enable him to be confident of his judgement, he may carry on and land; otherwise he must overshoot, and either enter the holding pattern pending another approach, or divert to an alternative airport. During the approach, the pilot's line of sight is down the glidepath and not along the runway, and this gives rise to another factor, called 'slant visual range', which a pilot must take into account in order to avoid misinterpretation of visual cues.

ICAO categorisation

The foregoing terms are related in a system of categorisation adopted by ICAO, and which describes low-visibility landing capabilities based on the principle that the probability of having adequate short visual reference, for the range of permitted decision heights, should be as high as possible. The definitions of the main categories are graphically illustrated in fig. 9.1.

The three categories also serve as an indication of the stages through which automatic approach and automatic landing development progresses, and thereby designate the capabilities of individual automatic flight control systems. In addition, they designate the standards of efficiency of the ground guidance equipment available at airports, namely, ILS localiser and glide path, and approach, runway and taxiway lighting.

In connection with automatic landing systems, and in describing low weather minima, the term 'all weather operations' is frequently used; a term which can, and sometimes is, taken to mean that there are no weather conditions that can prevent an aircraft from taking-off and landing successfully. This is not the case, because no automatic system can, for example, perform the landing task in wind conditions in excess of those for which the aircraft has been certificated, this being primarily governed by the controllability characteristics and strength factors of the aircraft. Similarly, no automatic system can land an aircraft on a runway the surface of which, because of water, slush or ice, is not fit for such an operation.

System reliability and redundancy

In chapter 7 (page 180) details were given of the purpose and operation of devices designed to limit the authority of automatic control systems in the event of 'runaway' conditions resulting from malfunctions. While

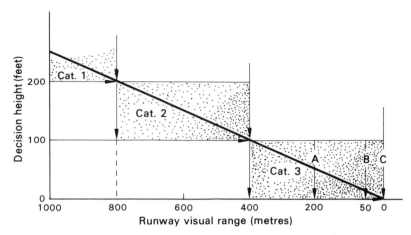

Category 1: Operation down to minima of 200 ft decision height and runway visual range of 800 m with a high probability of approach success.

Category 2: Operation down to minima below 200 ft decision height and runway visual range of 800 m, and to as low as 100 ft decision height and runway visual range of 400 m with a high probability of approach success.

Category 3A: Operation down to and along the surface of the runway, with external visual reference during the final phase of the landing down to runway visual range minima of 200 m.

Category 3B: Operation to and along the surface of the runway and taxiways with visibility sufficient only for visual taxiing comparable to runway visual range value in the order of 50 m.

Category 3C: Operation to and along the surface of the runway and taxiways without external visual reference.

Fig. 9.1 Categories of low-visibility landings

such devices may be incorporated in the more conventional control systems, and thereby be generally effective for the intended purpose down to 'break-off' heights, i.e. approach heights at which a control system is disengaged, this would not satisfy the requirements for systems designed for autolanding. For example, if an aircraft is on the glide path and a 'runaway' occurs in the pitch control channel causing a nose-down attitude then obviously height will be lost, and in using a torque limiting device having a preset value, the aircraft could be well below the glide path before recovery can commence. Thus, there is a minimum altitude to which the device can be used.

The height lost following a malfunction could be reduced by a more severe limiting of control system authority. However, in cases where the flight path may be subject to disturbances resulting from turbulence and wind shear, the situation arises of having to apply rapid correction to the flight path leading to a demand for servomotor torque greater than that allowed by the safety devices. Thus, the setting of safety devices is dictated by two conflicting requirements.

1. They must limit the effect of a 'runaway' such that safe recovery can be effected by the pilot;

2. They must allow sufficient authority to the control system so that the required flight path can be followed accurately in the presence of disturbances.

Even with a compromise setting of a safety device, there is the possibility of a height loss under 'runaway conditions', which during an automatic landing would be unacceptable.

A further factor which limits the application of safety devices in the manner of conventional control systems, is their inability to protect against passive failures. While not producing flight path changes directly, these failures would nevertheless mean that the predetermined and accurate flight manoeuvre of automatic landing could not be maintained and so set up an equally dangerous situation.

It follows therefore, that to achieve the objective of automatic landing, the operation of an automatic flight control system must be of such a nature that it will:

1. not disturb the flight path as a result of an active malfunction;

2. have adequate authority for sufficiently accurate control along the required flight path;

3. warn of a passive failure;

4. not fail to complete the intended flight manocuvre following an active or a passive failure.

In order to resolve the problems which would otherwise have been associated with the application of the more conventional flight control systems, it was considered necessary to adopt the concept of 'system redundancy', i.e. to utilise multiple systems operating in such a manner that a single failure within a system will have an insignificant effect on the aircraft's performance during the approach and landing operation.

In describing failures and the system redundancy concept, it is inevitable that certain terminology must be adopted. It is therefore relevant at this point to review the accepted definitions.

Fail-soft is used to describe the ability of a system to withstand a failure without endangering passenger safety, and without producing excessive deviations from the flight path. An equivalent term adopted in the U.S.A. is *fail-passive*.

Fail-operational. This describes a system in which one failure (sometimes more) can occur, but leaves the overall system still functioning, and without causing degradation of performance beyond the limits required for automatic landing and roll-out. Alternative terms are: *fail-active* and *failure-survival*.

Simplex. This term is usually used to define a single automatic control system and its appropriate number of sub-channels. Although various elements of the system may be duplicated, a single failure elsewhere will result in complete unserviceability. In the U.S.A., the equivalent term *single (non-redundant)* is used.

Multiplex. This term is applied to a system comprising two or more sensibly independent simplex systems and sub-channels used collectively so that, in the event of a failure of a system or sub-channel, the remaining systems are alone capable of performing the controlling function. The number of systems and sub-channels adopted is qualified by the terms duplex, triplex and quadruplex as appropriate.

Duplex system is a system of two complete systems or channels which are interconnected, and which together provide continuous control. If comparison monitoring is provided, a duplex system can provide fail-operational capability. The term should not be confused with the terms duplicated-monitored or duplicate-redundancy. An equivalent term adopted in the U.S.A. is *dual active with passive monitoring*.

Triplex system is a fail-operational system of three complete systems or channels which are interconnected and which together provide continuous control. In the event of failure of one of the systems or channels, that system or channel is outvoted by the other two and is automatically disengaged; control is therefore continued in duplex. In the event of a further fault in either of the two remaining systems or channels, they will both disconnect, and the aircraft is returned to the pilot in a trimmed and safe attitude. An equivalent term used in the U.S.A. is *triple-redundant*.

Duplicate-monitored. This refers to a system comprising two systems in parallel and with separate power supplies. The components of both are designed to be either self-monitoring or to have their outputs checked by parallel comparator circuits. Only one system is engaged at any particular time, the other system being in a follow-up mode, and thereby serving as an active standby. In the event of a fault being shown up by the self-monitors or comparators of either of the systems, control is automatically changed over to the standby system.

Dual-dual. This term is used by some manufacturers to define a twin fail-operational control system having twin passive monitoring systems. It should not be considered synonymous to a duplex system, since the control systems may or may not be active simultaneously. In the event of a monitor detecting a failure in its associated system, the second system with its monitor is switched in.

Monitoring. In its strictest sense and, in particular, when applied to multiplex systems, this term defines the process of making comparisons either between two or more outputs (or inputs) or between an output (or input) and a selected datum. The monitoring process can also assume a limiting function; e.g. when it is set up to cause a system to disconnect whenever an output (or input) exceeds a prescribed limit.

Comparison monitor is one which operates on data supplied from comparable stages in two or more similar systems.

Equaliser. This is a device which adjusts the performance of the subsystems in multiplex systems to remove differences between sub-system outputs that may arise other than as a result of fault conditions. Two devices are normally adopted, one called a *gain equaliser* which adjusts the amplitude of response of sub-systems, and the other called a *datum equaliser* which adjusts the steady state output of sub-systems.

Approach and autoflare

Autoflare provides automatic or flight director control between the lowest part of the glide path, established by the ILS, and touchdown. The nature of the control is divided into four phases as shown in fig. 9.2. At glide phase 1, the automatic flight control system and the flight director are coupled to the ILS glide path receivers, i.e. the aircraft is on a conventional 'coupled approach'. The signals are continuously monitored by a deviation signal comparator, and the signal ultimately selected is fed to all three pitch computers which compute the attitude demand signals for the control servo system and the flight director. The latter displays the attitude of the aircraft with respect to the glide path. At an appropriate altitude (about 1,000 feet) during glide phase 1 of the descent, a selector on the flight controller is set to 'LAND', and this allows additional pitch rate terms to be computed to compensate for aerodynamic effects resulting from, say, wind gusts, selection of flaps, and airspeed changes, and thereby reduces any tendency for the aircraft to depart from the glide path.

At glide phase 2, and approximately 350 feet above ground level, a signal from radio altimeters causes the gain of the glide path receiver signals to be reduced, i.e. a 'beam gearing change' takes place to compensate for the fact that the width of the beam narrows nearer to the ground.

The third or 'attitude' phase, is initiated at approximately 140 feet when a discriminant signal from the radio altimeters causes the

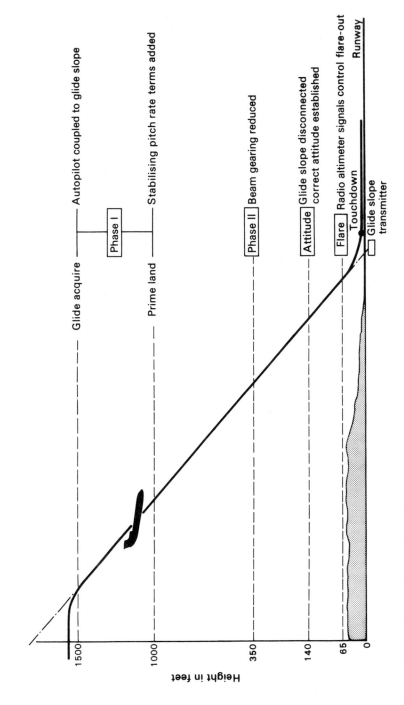

Fig. 9.2 Glide path coupling and autoflare

computed glide path signals to be disconnected from the control servo system, and to be substituted by radio altimeter demand signals. The signals are derived in the pitch computers from integration of the aircraft pitch rate over the previous part of the approach. Thus, a mean glide path attitude of the aircraft is sustained until the aircraft is low enough to start flaring out.

The attitude phase of control continues down to 65 feet, at which height, the fourth or 'flare' phase is initiated and pitch demand signals are supplied solely by the radio altimeters, so that the rate of descent is reduced in proportion to the height. Also at the height of 65 feet, the autothrottle system ceases to maintain airspeed and closes the throttles. At 12 feet, the rudder control channels, which up to this stage provide yaw damping, are coupled to the compass systems so that the aircraft's heading is then continually aligned with the runway in response to heading error signals. The rudder control channels operate only at the duplex level since there is no need for a fail-operational capability about the yaw axis.

On touchdown, the pilot disconnects the whole automatic flight control system by means of the cut-out switches on the control wheel, and then carries out the procedures for conventional manual ground-roll guidance. For aircraft that are cleared for full automatic approach and automatic landing operations, e.g. Category 3B conditions, the rudder control channel is not disconnected when the cut-out switch is activated, and the pilot is assisted by an automatic guidance and ground-roll monitoring system.

Radio altimeters

From the foregoing brief description of the automatic approach and autoflare phases of flight, two essential differences between them and conventional automatic control systems will have been noted. Firstly, the obvious difference that control is automatic right down to the landing, and secondly, that vertical guidance to touchdown in response to ILS glide path signals is dispensed with at, and below, a certain height, and is substituted by guidance in response to radio altimeter signals.

The reasons for terminating glide path signal guidance are that, below 140 feet, the signals tend to become unstable; the convergence of the glide path beam presents coupling difficulties as a result of necessary beam gearing changes; and the slope of the beam is too abrupt for a safe and comfortable landing to be made. In order, therefore, to ensure more accurate control of the aircraft's rate of descent, and smoother flareout, the system is designed to reduce the rate of descent in proportion to the height of the aircraft such that the vertical component of its flight path follows an exponential curve starting from the glide path. This requires continuous and accurate measurement of height, such measurement being accomplished by a radio altimeter system.

Ground-roll control

In a conventional manual landing sequence, and subsequent to touchdown on the runway, the pilot must control the aircraft during the ground roll so that the aircraft will be brought to a standstill on, or close to, the runway centreline. Control is effected by means of the rudder, nose wheel steering system and braking system, the latter being assisted by the reversal of engine thrust.

As far as an automatic landing is concerned, it is thus apparent that the sequence can only be considered complete when the system employed can also provide automatic directional control along the runway without any external visual guidance. The system designed specifically for 'Trident' aircraft again serves as the example of how automatic landings have been carried out in commercial operations cleared for Category 3A conditions.

On touchdown, the pitch and roll control channels are disengaged leaving the rudder control channel to provide directional control by means of signals from the ILS localiser and the compass systems, such signals having been coupled to the rudder control channel at a height of 12 feet. In the first stage of the ground roll, and down to a speed of 80 knots, braking is effected by using reverse thrust. At 80 knots, the rudder control channel is automatically disengaged, and the pilot takes over directional control of the aircraft by the use of nose wheel steering, and brings the aircraft to a stand-still, or a slow taxiing speed, by conventional use of the wheel brakes.

In this second stage of the ground roll as well as in the stages preceding the landing, the pilot must have accurate directional information presented to him from flight director instruments, and in such a way as to help overcome one of the most difficult problems to be faced during an approach and landing sequence in low visibility conditions, namely the transition from instrument flight to visual flight. The display method adopted in the 'Trident' system is known as a Para-Visual Display (PVD) and is a simplex unmonitored director the operation of which is based on the fact that the human eye, when fixed on some distant object, can still perceive movements of objects in the general field of view; such perception is through that part of the retina of the eye known as the parafovea, which surrounds the area of fixated vision.

A PVD unit is shown in fig. 9.3. It consists of a motor-driven cylinder

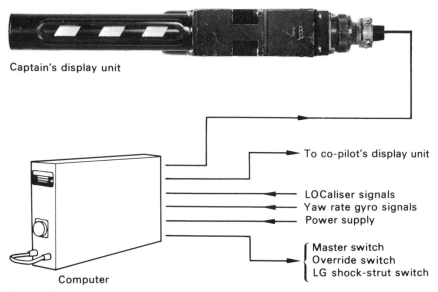

Captain's display unit

To co-pilot's display unit

LOCaliser signals
Yaw rate gyro signals
Power supply

Master switch
Override switch
LG shock-strut switch

Computer

Fig. 9.3 Para-visual display system

with a black and white helix painted along its length, part of this pattern being visible through a narrow window in the cylinder casing. A coupled tachogenerator provides a feedback signal such that the rate at which the cylinder revolves is proportional to the command signals. A shutter is provided which automatically, exposes or obscures, the display appropriate to selected operating modes. Command signals are supplied to the motor from the ILS localiser receiver and yaw rate gyro, after processing by a computer. The unit is mounted on the glare shield panel so that its indications are within the pilot's general field of view, when he is looking either at the flight instruments on the main instrument panel (head-down) or looking through the windscreen (head-up).

As noted earlier, the rudder control channel is automatically disengaged when the aircraft's speed during the ground roll has decreased to 80 knots. At the same time, the shutter of the PVD unit is automatically operated to expose the cylinder, and the driving motor remains connected only to the source of ILS localiser signals. If the aircraft is on the runway centreline there are no command signals from the computer, and so the PVD unit cylinder remains static, and the pilot monitors the progress of the ground roll, correcting it through the medium of the nosewheel steering system, to ensure that the static condition is maintained. If the aircraft deviates from the runway centreline, to the left say, a signal from the appropriate part of the localiser beam will be transmitted to the PVD unit, causing the cylinder to rotate in such a direction that the pilot will observe, within his general field of view, a black and white striped pattern 'streaming' to the right; the pilot is therefore, commanded to 'steer to the right' until the PVD unit is once again static. Deviation of the aircraft to the right of the runway centreline has the opposite effect on the PVD unit and its display.

In the development of ground-roll control and guidance techniques in low-visibility conditions, it was also found necessary to provide information on the aircraft's speed along the runway, and on the distance-to-go from touchdown; in addition to the PVD unit therefore, a Ground-Roll Monitoring (GRM) system is provided. The system consists of two wheel pick-off units, and a combined indicator/computer (see fig. 9.4).

Wheel pick-off   Indicator/computer

Fig. 9.4 Ground-roll monitoring system

Each wheel pick-off unit consists of a two-pole soft-iron rotor mounted on a shaft and rotating inside a two-phase stator. One phase of the stator is supplied with 26 volts a.c. at 400 Hz from the indicator/computer unit, while the other phase provides an output of four cycles of 100% modulation of the main supply of 115 volts a.c., for each revolution of the rotor and aircraft wheel. A pick-off unit is located at each main landing gear, its rotor being driven by one of the wheels through an appropriate form of shaft coupling. This mounting arrangement ensures that recording of distance is instantaneous the moment a wheel touches the runway and spins-up.

The indicator is basically a milliammeter providing a 180° scale presentation of ground speed from o to 100 knots, the meter being integrated with a digital counter providing a readout of the distance-to-go up to a total possible indication of 9,990 metres. When the readout reaches 0000, a detector operates to stop further counting while the speed continues to be indicated. Setting of the counter to a required distance is accomplished by means of the setting control knob in the lower left-hand corner of the indicator bezel. The knob can be rotated from its spring-loaded centre detent position to either of two positions anti-clockwise and indicated S— and F—, or to either of two positions clockwise and indicated S+ and F+. These positions respectively permit slow or fast downward-counting settings, or slow or fast upward-counting settings to be made. At the same time, they provide a confidence check on the operation of the ground speed indicator since, in either of the S positions, the indicator pointer will remain at zero and, in either of the F positions, the pointer will move to indicate approximately 100 knots within a green arc marked on the indicator scale.

A red warning lamp is provided in the upper left-hand corner of the indicator bezel, and serves as a monitor of pick-off operation, by illuminating whenever the time delay between the receipt of signal pulses from the pick-off units exceeds seven seconds. The seven second delay allows for situations where one landing gear wheel touches down before the other. To prove the integrity of the warning circuit, the lamp is also illuminated when the distance-to-go setting control knob is held away from its centre detent position for more than seven seconds. The knob in the upper right-hand corner of the indicator bezel actuates a two-position push-pull switch; when pushed in, the switch completes the signal circuits between the pick-off units and distance-to-go counter, and when the switch is pulled out, it inhibits operation of the counter thereby 'fixing' its indication to the selected value.

Prior to landing, the pilot positions the setting control knob so that the distance-to-go counter will operate until it indicates the value required. Since different types of aircraft touchdown on a runway at varying distances from the threshold, the value to be set on the counter is equal to the runway length minus the distance to the touchdown point. The knob in the upper right-hand corner of the indicator is pushed in to connect the pick-off units to the counter, and in order to ensure that there will be no premature counting-down due to 'wind-milling' of the wheels prior to touchdown, the datum from which counting commences is automatically raised by a pre-determined value (10 knots in the case of the 'Trident' system). When the wheels start to rotate, the pick-off units produce pulses (4 per wheel revolution) which are fed to the computer for counting and scaling by the appropriate sections of the circuit, and then to the counter in which they progressively subtract from the preset distance until this distance has been travelled. At this stage, the counter will indicate zero, and the counting circuit will be automatically deactivated until the counter is reset.

The signal circuits are so arranged that the system automatically locks itself to whichever pick-off unit is the first to provide a signal pulse. Thus, no distance-to-go information is lost, and since the system will function with only one pick-off unit operational, some redundancy is also provided. The pick-off pulses are also processed and integrated by relevant circuits of the computer to derive ground speed information which is displayed on the milliammeter simultaneously with distance-to-go information. The amplitude of the pulses is preset by an external link adjustment so that they are matched to the sizes of the aircraft's wheels.

As noted earlier, the rudder control channel of the automatic control system, is disconnected during the ground roll at a speed of 80 knots. This is accomplished by also applying the scaled pulses required for ground speed computation to a logic circuit which detects pulses equivalent to 80 knots, and energises a relay in the rudder control channel circuit. The relay is also energised when the brakes are applied to the main landing gear wheels after take-off, but since the disengage signal circuit for the rudder control channel is supplied via landing gear shock-strut microswitches, which remain open under no-load conditions of the struts, energising of the relay will have no effect on the rudder control channel. Nevertheless, if the ground roll monitoring system is left switched on after take-off and is inadvertently not reset for the subsequent landing, an immediate rudder control channel disconnect will occur when the aircraft touches down and the shock-strut microswitches are activated. Resetting is effected by moving the setting knob momentarily out of its detent position.

At very low ground speeds, where a minimal speed indication might not be sufficiently apparent, it is desirable to introduce a more positive method of display. Accordingly, below five knots, individual wheel pulses are fed direct to the ground speed indicator causing the pointer to give a substantial 'kick' at each quarter revolution of the wheels.

Equalisation

The multiplex operation of an automatic flight control system demands that the sub-systems and channels be substantially identical in order to give the same control laws. It is inevitable, however, that some differences in system and channel outputs will arise due entirely to tolerances; tolerance effects must be taken into account in the overall design, therefore, so that disengagement of a system or channel will occur only under genuine fault conditions, and not within the allowable tolerance bands which would give rise to what is termed 'nuisance tripping'. Thus, the performance of sub-systems and channels must be continuously and automatically adjusted, the adjustment process being termed equalisation.

Many factors can contribute to variations in performance between sub-systems and channels, but the variation produced can always be considered as either a variation in datum, or a variation in gain. Datum equalisation is required to provide corrective action which must be both short-term (or instantaneous) and long-term (or average). Gain equalisation is essentially a short-term requirement. The following details are again based on the equalisation methods adopted in the Smith's Series 5/Trident flight control system, and are intended to serve only as an example of the application of the fundamental principles generally involved. For convenience, descriptions are confined to operation as a duplex system; triplex operation follows the same lines, and the differences will be noted later.

Datum equalisation

Equalisation is achieved by feeding into each servo amplifier input (see fig. 9.5) a limited signal proportional to the difference between the two servo amplifier outputs, the difference resulting from datum errors. This symmetrical arrangement produces immediate equal and opposite adjustment in both sub-channels thereby causing a change in the performance of either of them. The net result is that the amplifier outputs are brought almost to the average output level. A small residual difference must remain, however, in order to sustain the feedback action, but this difference is not sufficient to cause torque opposition between the sub-channels. By limiting the amount of feedback which can be employed, the system ensures that the difference between the datum inputs (A and B in fig. 9.5) cannot exceed a predetermined level if equalisation is to be effected. If no fault condition exists this level will never be exceeded, but it is possible under fault conditions, for datum inputs A and B, to be outside the permissible limits, while the difference between the inputs is acceptable to the equalisation circuits.

The adjustment process thus far described is referred to as short-term datum equalisation, but this alone is not sufficient for applying corrective action since it is possible for it to mask a fault condition. It is, therefore, necessary to employ long-term equalisation, and as will be noted from fig. 9.5, in addition to the short-term feedback, the residual difference in amplifier outputs is also fed back as a proportional time

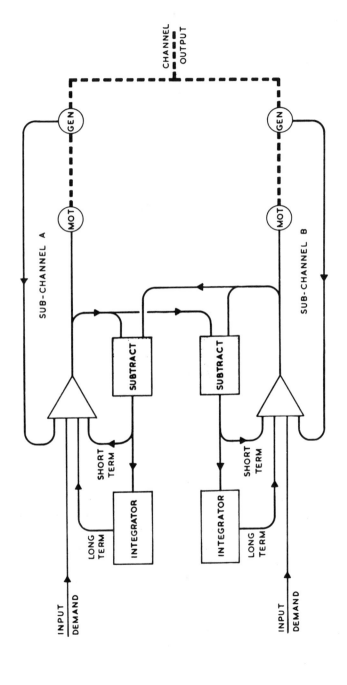

Fig. 9.5 Datum equalisation

integrated signal, via an integrator, or datum balancer. Thus, the residual difference is further reduced until eventually the output of each servo amplifier is brought to the precise average datum output.

Although exact datum equalisation is achieved, however, the effect of the datum inputs is not eliminated and this causes the flight control surfaces associated with the particular control channel to be driven at a small constant rate proportional to the average datum error. As a result, the surfaces drift steadily away from the desired position until such time as a manoeuvre demand signal is created, which exactly balances the average datum demand to bring each servo amplifier output to zero. The departure of the aircraft from the desired attitude or manoeuvre is therefore halted, but a standing error is set up.

To eliminate the effects the standing error would have on the aircraft attitude, the error signal is processed in computers of the sub-channels, to provide long-term balance signal inputs to the integrators of the datum equalisation circuits. As the integrator outputs build up, the control surfaces are driven in the reverse direction causing the standing error to decrease. This results in a decrease of the manoeuvre demand, and long-term inputs, until the error is reduced to zero, at which point the system stabilises with a net zero demand on the flight control surfaces. The net input to each servo amplifier, i.e. the sub-channel datum input together with the integrator input, is also zero, and consequently each integrator provides an input which is equal and opposite to the sub-channel datum input. In this particular application, the integrators are of the electro-mechanical type and the positions of their output shafts represent the absolute datum drift of each sub-channel.

Gain equalisation

During automatic manoeuvring of the aircraft, large signal levels can be produced, and as a result it is possible that the difference between channel signals may exceed the authority of the short-term datum equalisation circuits. It becomes necessary to adjust automatically the gain of these circuits, therefore, and this is achieved by comparing the amplifier output voltages in the sub-channels, and then adjusting the rate feedback signals from the servomotor tachogenerators. Fig. 9.6 shows the arrangement adopted in duplex operation. Gain equalisation is essentially a short-term requirement.

Each sub-channel contains a gain equaliser which comprises a subtracting circuit, a feedback sense detector circuit, a multiplying circuit, and an excitation control circuit. Signals proportional to the outputs of the two servo amplifiers are fed to both the subtracting circuits. The output of each subtracting circuit is equal to the output of

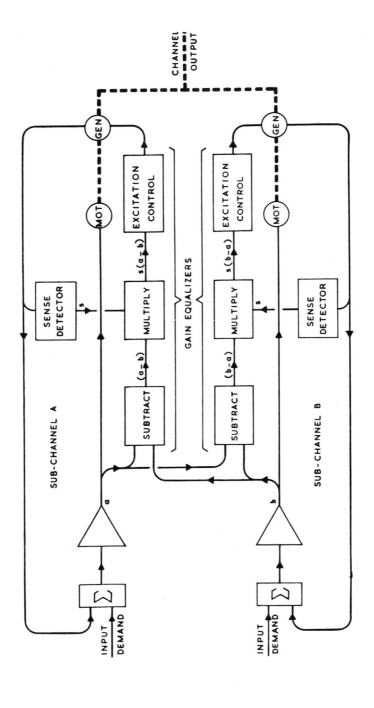

Fig. 9.6 Gain equalisation

the amplifier in the other sub-channel. This means that the difference signals in the two sub-channels are equal in amplitude but opposite in sense. The difference signal is then multiplied by a signal of unity amplitude and of the same sense as the rate feedback signal. As the servomotor output shafts must rotate in the same direction, the feedback sense is the same in each of the sub-channels. The sense of the resulting product determines whether the gain of a sub-channel is to be increased or decreased, and the amplitude of the product determines the extent of the gain change.

The product is supplied to an excitation control network which, in turn, is connected to its relevant servomotor tachogenerator; thus, the excitation supply can be either increased or decreased. An increase in the supply results in a reduction of gain, and vice versa. In the event of a variation in performance of either of the sub-channels, then due to symmetry of the system, equal and opposite adjustment occurs simultaneously in both of the channels. The result is that the difference in performance, and equalisation, is reduced, and the system stabilises with acceptable torque opposition, well below the level at which the servomotor torque limiting device operates.

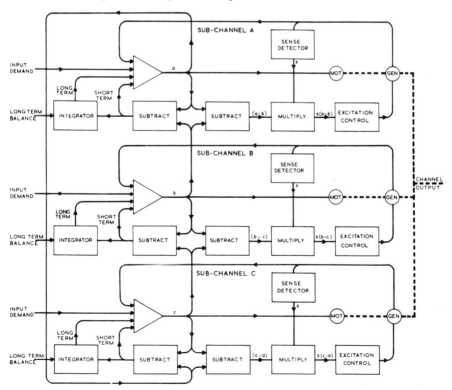

Fig. 9.7 Triplex equalisation

Triplex equalisation

The datum and gain equalisation circuits for triplex operation are shown in fig. 9.7. The operating principles are the same as those adopted for operation in duplex, except that comparison between sub-channels is effected by comparing sub-channel A with sub-channel B, sub-channel B with sub-channel C, and sub-channel C with sub-channel A. If a fault in one sub-channel causes that channel to disengage, automatic switching ensures that the interconnections between sub-channels are altered to provide duplex operation.

Sensor equalisation

This is an adjustment process adopted in the Series 5/Trident system, and is applied to the radio altimeter signal circuits. The altitude signals are derived from three radio altimeters, and because each altimeter is not 'looking at' the same area of ground below the aircraft, the signals tend to be 'noisy'; equalisation is necessary to cater for these effects, and also for tolerance effects. It is accomplished by using a circuit which arranges that the input to each sub-channel of the automatic flight control system is the average of the three radio altimeter inputs, providing that the signal added to each sub-channel does not exceed 8 feet. Should the difference between one altimeter and the other two exceed 8 feet, then the faulty altimeter signal is isolated, and the system sub-channel disconnected.

Autothrottle system

An autothrottle system serves the dual purpose of maintaining constant airspeed during automatic approach and landing phases by adjustments of engine power, and closing the throttles at a constant rate during an autoflare phase. A typical throttle control system is schematically illustrated in fig. 9.8.

Airspeed information is supplied from an air data computer via a control transformer link, the actual speed values being compared with a datum airspeed, this being the one at which the system was engaged. Differences between the two values produce error signals which are fed to the servo amplifiers and, after amplification, to the throttle servomotors. Thus, assuming that an error signal is produced in response to a decrease in airspeed, the servomotors will be activated to cause the throttles to open by an amount proportional to the error signal amplitude. As the airspeed of the aircraft slowly increases, the error signals are reduced and the throttles moved to the closed position. The throttles are not returned to the original positions, since a higher

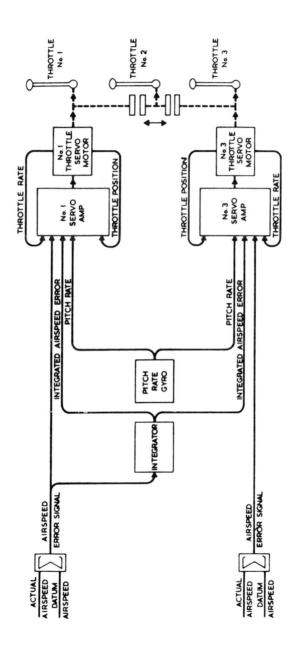

Fig. 9.8 Autothrottle system

amount of thrust is required to overcome the drag resulting from the higher airspeed.

As in any servo system, the error signals must be balanced by feedback signals, the signals in this case, being relevant to throttle servomotor position and rate of position change. Thus, the total input to the servo amplifiers is reduced to zero and a point is reached at which throttle actuation ceases, but some airspeed error remains. The residual error is corrected by passing the signal through an integrator circuit. Changes in airspeed resulting from changes in pitch attitude are anticipated by means of a rate-of-pitch-attitude-change signal which is applied to the servo amplifiers by a pitch rate gyroscope.

In a number of current types of public transport category aircraft, autothrottle systems have been introduced the operation of which is directed principally towards the conservation of fuel. The elements and data sources for one such system (employed in the Boeing 747) are shown schematically in fig. 9.9. In conjunction with a Total Air Temperature/Engine Pressure Ratio limit system (TAT/EPR) the complete autothrottle system provides three primary control modes: (i) EPR control; (ii) Mach hold; and (iii) speed control. In the first of these, the autothrottle commands the engine thrust levers so that the engine with the highest EPR, i.e. the ratio of engine inlet pressure to exhaust gas pressure, acquires and maintains the EPR limit value for the selected mode minus any increment of EPR decrease selected. The computer continuously compares all four engine EPRs and selects the one with the highest value as the controlling unit. The EPR mode is used during take-off, climb and go-around, and can also be used for maximum continuous thrust, and for cruise flight.

In the Mach hold function, which is used during cruise flight, the Mach number is held at the value at which the system was engaged. The speed control mode is used to acquire and maintain a selected airspeed, normally for descent, holding, approach and landing. The speed is indicated on a fast/slow speed scale of the attitude direction indicator of the flight director system. The selected value is indicated on the mode selector panel of the automatic flight control system, and also by a 'bug' on the captain's and first officer's airspeed indicators.

Sub-modes are also available to provide additional control or protection, including take-off, overboost protection, minimum speed protection (provided by angle of attack sensors) and flap speed limit protection which automatically limits the maximum speed that can be commanded by the autothrottle system to a value determined by flap position.

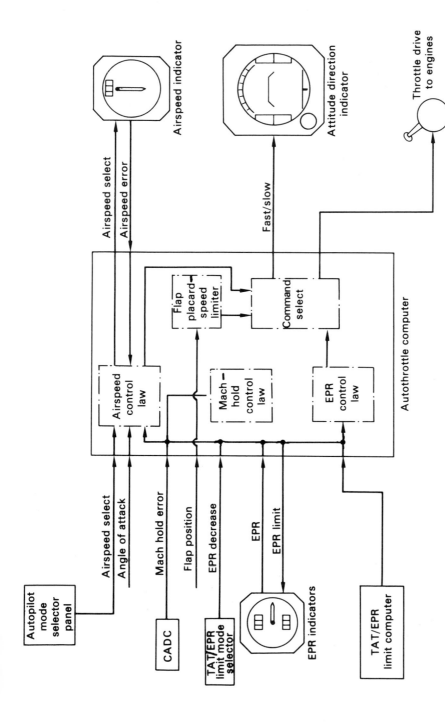

Fig. 9.9 Element and data sources of TAT/EPR autothrottle system

Index